What Patients Love

What Patients Love

Press Ganey's Guide to HCAHPS®

Press Ganey Associates, Inc.

What Patients Love: Press Ganey's Guide to HCAHPS® (HCAHPS® is a registered trademark of the Agency for Healthcare Research and Quality)

Library of Congress Cataloging-in-Publication Data

What Patients Love: Press Ganey's Guide to HCAHPS®, Press Ganey Associates

Library of Congress Control Number:		2007900722
ISBN:	Hardcover	978-1-4257-5587-4
	Softcover	978-1-4257-5548-5

1. Patient satisfaction. 2. Medical care surveys. 3. Medical care—Quality control. 4. Communication.

Published by: Press Ganey
404 Columbia Place South Bend, IN 46601
www.pressganey.com

Compiled by: Press Ganey Associates (Special thanks to those who submitted stories: Jodie Cunningham, Beth Heck, Michelle Gloss, Laura Lindberg, Julie Tabler, Renee Doren, Kendra Ciszczon, Linda Paustian, Melissa Thatcher, Katie Drevs, Laura Duman, David Truax, Dave Trowbridge, Kelly Wright, Tobeter Towne, Jennifer Snyder, Barb Huffer, Bethany Pointer, Lisa Daul, Aris Relias, Peter Lanser, Paul Clark, Martin Wright, Julie Piatkowski, Amy Frederick, Shelley Barger and Heather Frederick. Also, special thanks to our clients who share their stories every day.)
Edited by: Kelley Shrock
Proofed by: Kelley Shrock, Paul Clark and Maxwell Drain

Press Ganey helps thousands of health care organizations improve the quality of care they provide by offering the following:

- Standard and customized surveying tools
- Electronic and manual reporting
- Advanced survey printing, mailing, and processing services
- Experience and expertise in quality improvement
- Best practices
- Guidance toward solutions

As the clear market leader, our services are built on a fundamental commitment to quality improvement. We guide your organization to solutions by providing the latest research, high-quality survey instruments, technological innovation, and customer service.

To request information on Press Ganey's services or to order more copies of this or other guides, please visit *www.pressganey.com.*

This book was printed in the United States of America.

To order additional copies of this book, contact:
Press Ganey Associates, Inc.
1-800-232-8032
pressganey.com
WhatPatientsLove@pressganey.com
Or, contact a Press Ganey consultant or sales representative.
37549

Contents

Introduction

"Measurement leadership like that provided by Press Ganey can be a basis for feeding into the further development of publicly reported consensus measures, as a basis for reimbursement as well as for supporting consumer choice systems that private plans implement or the government implements in Medicare. And with a broader internal set of analyses and measures that underlie the publicly reported measures, the hospitals that participate in more intensive measurement efforts can have a better understanding of why they're performing the way they are performing and how they can improve in their measured performance."

—Dr. Mark McClellan, former Administrator of
the Centers for Medicare and Medicaid Services,
on Press Ganey and HCAHPS®.

Our health care system constantly evolves. Thanks in part to the Internet, patients have more access to information about medical facilities, physicians, illnesses and treatments than ever before. Empowered patients are able to be more involved in their care and can make well-reasoned decisions. Public report cards, like HCAHPS, represent the next step in this evolution towards a more market-oriented health care system.

Many believe that the publicly-reported information on hospital quality and patient satisfaction will change how patients select their health care providers. While that may be true for many consumers, others will continue to trust their friends' and families' recommendations over information from any other source. Patients have *always* held providers accountable for performance through negative word-of-mouth and by voting with their own two feet. Regardless, the challenge before all of us is how to improve health care delivery and satisfy patients. HCAHPS and Press Ganey can help chart the course.

In this book, Press Ganey authors examine health care experiences through a unique lens—that of an educated observer. Press Ganey has a universal perspective of the health care industry by surveying 10 million patients, almost 200,000 employees and tens of thousands of physicians at more than 7,000 health care facilities across the country. This book will help providers understand how their work affects patients and their families. By reflecting on and understanding the impact that care and actions have on patients, provider and facility practices can be amended and patient care improved.

Press Ganey's team has passionately promoted the voice of patients for the past two decades. HCAHPS shines an additional spotlight on patients' satisfaction. We know that patient satisfaction is related to clinical quality (i.e., satisfied patients are more compliant, better understand their therapy regimens, and encounter safer environments). At Press Ganey, we work not simply for the patient's sake, but also for the sake of people working in health care—doctors, nurses, and everyone on the front lines.

HCAHPS is not something that just happens to us. We control our interaction with patients. We control the management policies, processes, and systems to deliver care. There is a reason Press Ganey's partners continuously win national quality awards at such a higher than expected rate. It's because of a predisposition to proactive action—embracing changes and doing more than the minimum necessary for simple compliance. Our customers are driven to be in the forefront of improving the delivery of health care.

Health care tomorrow will not remain exactly like it is today. We can create new practices that make it easier for providers to deliver care *and* to improve the quality of care that is delivered. Thank you for all that you do to make health care better.

Melvin F. Hall, PhD
President and CEO
Press Ganey Associates, Inc.

What Is HCAHPS®?

H CAHPS is a national standardized survey instrument designed to assess patients' perspectives of hospital care for public reporting purposes. Results will be reported on CMS' Web site. Currently, a hospital's eligibility for annual reimbursement increases is tied to whether the hospital participates in HCAHPS. In the future, monetary incentives or reimbursements may be tied to the level of performance of the hospital, not just the participation in reporting of results.

At the request of CMS, the Agency for Healthcare Research and Quality (AHRQ), a federal government agency within the Department of Health and Human Services (HHS), led the development of the survey in collaboration with stakeholder organizations, such as the National Quality Forum (NQF) and Press Ganey Associates.

The HCAHPS survey consists of 22 questions about a hospital stay with 5 background questions for a total of 27 survey items. On the survey, questions are divided into seven sections or headings: "Your Care from Nurses," "Your Care from Doctors," "The Hospital Environment," "Your Experiences in This Hospital," "When You Left the Hospital," "Overall Rating of Hospital," and the background section "About You" (for full instrument, see Appendix A) The questions from the HCAHPS instrument are combined into domains for public reporting. These domains differ from the headings that are listed on the survey itself. The publicly reported results will appear as seven domain scores and two global ratings:

- Domains:
    - o Communication with nurses
    - o Responsiveness of hospital staff
    - o Communication with doctors
    - o Cleanliness and quiet of physical environment
    - o Pain control

- o   Discharge information
- o   Communication about medicines

- • Global ratings:
  - o   Overall rating of the hospital
  - o   Extent to which patients are willing to recommend the hospital

Any adult patient discharged from a general acute care hospital for an acute stay may receive an HCAHPS survey. Patients are only excluded if they are under 18, did not stay overnight, had a non-acute stay (e.g., psychiatric, rehab or skilled nursing) or are excluded by a state law or regulation. Families of patients who died in the hospital do not receive the survey. HCAHPS surveys are randomly distributed to a sample of patients throughout the entire year which means that there isn't a set HCAHPS survey time. In other words, every patient interaction could be relevant to HCAHPS results.

How to Use This Book

We learn through stories. By telling true stories, this book shares the experiences and insights of Press Ganey consultants, clients and our professional network. Substantial, serious research went into designing HCAHPS and Press Ganey measures of the patient experience. The scientific rigor of these measurement systems serves as the foundation for our deep understanding of patients' hospitalization experiences. The decades spent assisting healthcare organizations make extraordinary improvements in their culture, processes, patient, and business outcomes has provided us with insight into what it takes to actually change an organization's total service delivery experience for patients.

The goal of this book is to help everyone in your facility understand HCAHPS, explain how what happens in real life translates into the measures reported by CMS, and help stimulate organizational change.

What we do in health care heavily depends on the quality of the interaction between people. The art of medicine and the art of service are neither innate nor automatic. These are skills that are acquired and refined only through practice. If we don't take time to reflect, examine our habits, and continuously strive to improve, our medical and service skills will atrophy.

In this spirit, these stories serve to spark changes in your practice, processes, and systems. To launch organizational change, use this book in the following ways:

- Start meetings with a story from *What Patients Love*. Discuss what it means to your practice, what you would do differently, and how you could apply the ideas.
- Use *What Patients Love* stories or your own stories to illustrate the importance of an organizational value or service standard.
- Act out a *What Patients Love* story in a live skit or recorded video for customer service training.
- Place *What Patients Love* in every break area or doctor's lounge.

- Give *What Patients Love* to every manager/area who is involved in the HCAHPS survey.
- Give *What Patients Love* to your CEO or other executives before they go on a trip with a note, "For the plane ride." When they return, ask what ideas they gleaned from it.
- Create your own *What Patients Love* book using your own patients' stories of successful encounters. Put copies in your waiting areas and sell them at local book stores with your organization's brand prominently displayed.

What Patients Love represents the start of changing your organization for the new HCAHPS era. Everyone can be a leader. When your patients' perspectives are public, everyone needs to be a leader. Consider this your call to action!

Chapter 1.

Communication with Nurses

How It's Measured

The domain "Communication with Nurses" is covered in the first three questions of the HCAHPS survey:

- ☑ During this hospital stay, how often did nurses treat you with <u>courtesy and respect?</u>
- ☑ During this hospital stay, how often did nurses <u>listen carefully to you?</u>
- ☑ During this hospital stay, how often did nurses <u>explain things</u> in a way you could understand?

Patients estimate the frequency of these behaviors by selecting one of four response options: Never, Sometimes, Usually, or Always.

Patients don't spend their hospital stay with scorecard in hand, marking down the frequency of these behaviors. They rely on perception and memory recall. The underlined portions of the sentence are designed to focus patients' memories on those elements: courtesy and respect, listening carefully, and explaining things. One extraordinarily negative or positive encounter may sway their response to one of the extremes.

The Patient's Perspective

Patients value communication with their nurses. Through communication, patients begin to understand their illness, the care we can provide to them, and their healthcare future.

Nurses value communication as well, but for different reasons. For nurses, communication has a specific purpose: information needs to be imparted. This is the task-oriented approach to communication—good for checking things off the list but not necessarily good for patient satisfaction.

Once information has been given, the task is typically considered completed. Little do we realize that for patients to remember this information, it needs to be **repeated**. Reinforcing important messages increase the likelihood of patient recall. **Explaining things** means that information is understood and remembered. We know from the science of adult learning that we're more likely to learn when information is repeated and available in multiple formats—audio, print, and video. Arming nurses with handouts, brochures, and other **educational tools** will help patients' perceptions of how well things are explained **and help them better understand what they are being told**.

Our task-oriented approach to communication also means that we rarely examine **how** we're communicating. Sometimes, when we're short staffed and under pressure, our attention to **courtesy and respect** evaporates. We're not always aware of the impressions we make with our body language or tone of voice. Furthermore, many habits and practices common in hospitals would be considered socially inappropriate anywhere else. We often forget how personally invasive our work is to patients—physically and emotionally. We forget that patients are people. Clear service standards, training, role-playing, and honest individual feedback help re-orient our behavior to keep it consistently courteous and respectful.

For example, what are we consistently saying and how do patients interpret this? A great example comes from former Emergency Department (ED) nurse Liz Jazweic. She always would tell patients, "Good luck!" Little did she realize that her hearty wish was actually interpreted negatively, akin to "Hope you make it" or "You're going to need some luck to get through this." Instead, she changed her self-script of closing a patient encounter to "Thank you for giving me an opportunity to serve you."

Finally, for patients to respond that staff "always" **listen carefully**, they must **perceive** that you are listening. You may be listening, but if your **behavior** doesn't indicate listening, patients will perceive that you aren't paying attention. Demonstrating that you're listening isn't a chore. Sitting down next to the patient or taking a moment to look them in the eye reduces the likelihood that patients will find the need to repeat themselves, talk to other nurses about the same thing, or hit the call button. Patient-centered listening reduces patient anxiety, making patients easier to work with. Our workload doesn't matter to patients. What matters is the knowledge that, right now, in this moment, your attention is totally focused on the patient. You care for this *person* and will do your best. More than anything else, that's the reassurance patients need to **feel** from you.

Our Stories

The Ground Rules
By Jodie Cunningham, Solutions Consultant

The following ground rules are patient satisfaction standards that come from one of the best-performing hospitals in the country.

Rule #1: Our operational issues are not the patient's problem.

The words poor staffing, short staffed, doing a double, and so on should never be spoken when discussing patient satisfaction scores. Nearly all health care organizations face these same challenges. They are challenges—not acceptable excuses.

Rule #2: Every patient is your patient. Every bell is your bell.

The phrases "That's not my patient," "That's not my bell," or "Your bell is on" are not allowed.

Rule #3: Patient satisfaction is based on the patient's perception and the patient's perception is their reality. When reviewing patient complaints, the commonly used response of "Well, that was their perception. That's not the way it happened" is not permitted.

Rule #4: The golden rule. Do unto others as you would have them do to you. Care for the patients as if they were your family. Do whatever it takes. Do whatever necessary to make a patient heal, happy, comfortable, and well.

> ☑ **Setting specific rules for your team makes expectations for behavior explicitly clear. Standards are the first step to creating a patient-centered culture.**

Welcome to Our Unit
By Kathy Dittmann, Coordinator, Service Excellence,
Mount Nittany Medical Center (State College, PA)

Our nursing units at Mount Nittany Medical Center (State College, PA) include a "welcome" card on the bedsides. The card is personalized with the patient's name, the nurse manager's electronic signature, and an electronic signature of the first name of each person in the unit (nursing, housekeeping, dietary, etc.). The back of the card features the following message: "Please let us know if you have any concerns, complaints, or special requests." It also includes the information about who to direct these questions or comments to: the nurse and/or nurse manager's phone numbers, the patient representative's phone number, and the pastoral care phone number.

> ☑ **Simple gestures can remove uncertainty, make the new surroundings less intimidating, and help patients feel cared for.**

First Touch: A Journey to Trusting Relationships

By Nancy Inderwiesen, RN, Lynn Hiegel, RN, and Ronda Manney, RN, Saint Joseph Health Center (Kansas City, MO)

Saint Joseph Health Center (Kansas City, MO), part of Carondelet and Ascension Health, made an organizationwide commitment to provide service with excellence to the community. The facility's Cardiac Care Unit (CCU) was chosen for the pilot of *First Touch*. Members of the unit named themselves *Pioneers*, because they planned to blaze a trail toward creating consistently memorable patient experiences.

The goal of *First Touch* was to establish and sustain a trusting rapport with patients and families by bonding through a time of presence (e.g., initial meeting and discussion that gives a personal touch to the visit, and shows patients that each member of the unit is there for them throughout the experience). Specifically, *First Touch* was defined as the initial nonclinical, personal contact the caregiver has with the patient. It begins with "hello" and ends with "goodbye."

Following are the key components of the *First Touch* approach:

- Scripts to guide nurses during contact with patients and each other.
- A trial run with patients and families for two weeks before staff training.
- "Pioneers" as workshop facilitators, conducting 90-minute sessions.

The CCU staff embraced it! One nurse observed the following:

> We are giving ourselves permission to practice nursing as we have always wanted to, but felt we couldn't because of too little time.

Their enthusiasm paid off in the results:

- Higher patient satisfaction after just two quarters
- Positive comments from patients and families
- Positive comments from physicians, leaders, and colleagues
- A positive increase in CCU staff retention

Nurses and physicians are now excited. They believe their patients will be better served with this approach. Patients and families feel healed in ways they appreciate and deserve.

The Pioneers found that establishing relationships with patients non-clinically through First Touch resulted in decreased use of patients' call lights because staff took care of their needs up-front. They also found that saying "Goodbye" and introducing the oncoming staff member provided for better transition and rapport with patients.

The Pioneers are monitoring their patient satisfaction survey data (using the Press Ganey Inpatient Survey) by looking at specific indicators: friendliness/courtesy of the nurses, prompt response to call light, nurses' attitude toward requests, attention to specific/personal needs, nurses kept you informed, staff address emotional/spiritual needs. They have already seen improved scores in all of these areas.

> ☑ **The initial "touch" or impression that a patient and his/her family get from the representatives of your facility can set the tone for how the patient's stay will proceed. Try to take the time to meet with the patient and patient's family members to give information and ask for questions. Be sure to end the visit with a follow-up session that allows for closure.**

A Challenge to Employees: Deliver Quality Care to Become the Provider of Choice

After Doctors Hospital (Columbus, OH) spent years floundering between the 50th and 60th percentile for Outpatient Services, the senior leadership challenged all employees to deliver the level of quality care that would propel the organization into a market leader position. The Outpatient Services Department accepted the challenge and rapidly produced a strategy to move it towards creating sustainable results and achieving the facility's goal of the 80th percentile.

Actionable Steps

The Customer Service Department developed a number of system processes and tools to assist the organization in achieving the desired results. A "Must Haves" framework was created to assist employees and includes:

- Rounding
- Service recovery

- Reward and recognition
- Key words at key times
- Staff meetings
- Post-visit call backs

Motivation through recognition

Of all the steps, perhaps the most meaningful was cultivating the capacity to reward and recognize each other for their achievements on a daily basis. In healthcare organizations, people do amazing and beautiful things every day. Recognition fuels our fire, inspiring perseverance and motivating high performance.

To establish a system-wide recognition program, the Steering Committee's Reward and Recognition subcommittee developed the *Power of 1* **recognition program** to signify one system, one recognition program and that one person can make a difference. Patients, staff, physicians, volunteers, etc., can nominate a person for a *Power of 1* award at any time, after observing the person making an extra effort to live the customer service standards, regardless of the person's job. Nomination forms and drop boxes are prominently located throughout each campus. Every *Power of 1* nominee is recognized at a staff meeting, and each honoree receives a *Power of 1* pin to commemorate his/her first nomination. For every five nominations earned, the employee receives a prize such as movie tickets or a gift card as a small reinforcement of the desired behaviors.

An annual OhioHealth **Customer Service Retreat** for invited staff, physicians, managers and executives features nationally-known speakers, OhioHealth best practices and award presentations. Sixty attended in 2000; 1,000 participated in the 2006 day-long program, with renowned customer service experts Drs. Tray Dunaway and Jay Kaplan. Press Ganey representatives also present, so staff can "hear and learn from the source." Attendance itself is a reward, with each hospital president receiving only a limited number of invitations to issue.

The day begins with a lively video, comprised of a one-minute customer service clip from each facility and featuring its staff and leadership. For the 2006 event's Academy Award theme, customer service messages were recreated from such cinema classics as "Forrest Gump," "Beauty and the Beast" and "The Good, the Bad and the Ugly." The lunch-time awards ceremony is the day's highlight. Awards are presented to individuals, teams and hospitals in five categories. Individual Service Champions, Physician Service Champions and Customer Service Team Success Stories are chosen by a system-wide committee, while Most Improved Patient Satisfaction and Highest Sustained Patient Satisfaction awards are determined by historical Press Ganey data.

Combining recognition, team-building, motivation and education, more than 100 OhioHealth staff earned attendance at **Press Ganey's 2005 National**

Conference. Managers whose areas scored above the 60th percentile for the past year were rewarded with participation. In addition, staff mentioned on a patient survey during a three-month period (this reinforced introducing yourself to the patient by name) had their names entered in a drawing, with three winners per campus selected to attend with both their supervisor and a guest. Many attendees were line staff who might otherwise never attend a national conference. Being selected is a point of pride, motivates people and engenders friendly competition. After the conference, a video was prepared and shown to staff throughout the system, further reinforcing OhioHealth's commitment to customer service, building momentum around service and recognizing conference attendees.

To maintain customer service momentum and top-of-mind awareness, department, operations and management meetings consistently begin with **customer service stories and recognition**.

Since there can never be too much recognition for outstanding customer service, numerous system-wide and facility-specific **reward and recognition programs** flourish. Even though the *Power of 1* is OhioHealth's primary recognition program, each campus is encouraged to adopt its own recognition efforts, involving staff in their development and implementation. Hospital-specific efforts have been as inexpensive as earning cafeteria drink certificates to as extensive as a Disney World trip. This creativity and ownership have been key components in maintaining service momentum, adding fun, variety and involvement.

Results

The strategies outlined above have proven to be very successful. Through commitment, focus and lots of hard work, OhioHealth went from the lowest to the highest patient satisfaction quartile. Doctors Hospital experienced four consecutive quarters of improved results above the 80th percentile. At the same time, the quality of clinical outcomes also improved. As a result, the hospital has experienced market share growth and increases in procedural volume. The facility has also correlated improved customer service with a higher level of physician satisfaction and financial performance.

> ☑ **Patients love being served by well-rewarded, emotionally-fulfilled employees. Each person recognizing someone for their good work every day isn't too much. In fact, it may not be enough.**

First, Install Whiteboards
By Beth Heck, Regional Service Manager

One of the easiest ways to keep patients informed is the use of whiteboards in the room. These can range from simple plain boards to more detailed design boards that can be purchased through manufacturers. Include the name and phone number of the nurse on duty, the attending physician, and a tentative schedule (e.g., tests, therapies, meal times, anticipated schedule). Other information that might be helpful is the patient's room number and phone number for any visitors, the name and phone number of the housekeeper on duty, information on the patient's diet, and contact information for the patient advocate. Lastly, add a note stating, "if there is anything that we can do, please let us know," and include a copy of the survey or information about the importance of giving their feedback.

☑ **Adding a whiteboard to the patient's room will help the patient feel informed as well as reduce potential questions they may have.**

Now, Use the Whiteboards
By Michelle M. Gloss, MS, System Consultant

During a recent hospitalization, I had the opportunity to give thought to my experience that started with an ED admittance and became a three-day stay. I found that keeping me informed seemed to be a challenge for the staff all around. No one knew how long it would be before I would be moved from the triage room to the exam room. In the exam room, no one could tell me when I would receive pain medication—despite reporting level-seven pain. They would only say "after the doctor sees you." When the doctor saw me, he gave me a window of four hours from the time he saw me to the time I would be receiving the computed tomography (CT) scan and said the nurse would be in "shortly" to ask about pain. I received no updates in between these times. Each time that door closed, it seemed as though I didn't exist any more.

The whiteboard in the room was well done. It clearly listed all categories: nurse's name, physician's name, time for radiology and labs, and anticipated discharge date and time. But no one ever used it! Instead of facilitating communication across the care team and with patients, all the whiteboard did was emphasize the fact that the staff weren't keeping me informed. From this, I concluded that keeping the patient informed wasn't a priority for the staff.

What else could have been done to help me feel informed? Someone could have come to my room at least once per hour to update me on how my case was progressing. Even if I had to be pushed back in the queue, I would have been much more satisfied with the service and communication if I had been kept aware. If someone said, "I know that I told you last time that you were number three in line for an ultrasound, but we just had a patient arrive in premature labor. Your scan has been delayed for another hour. Do you need any more pain medication right now? Is there anything else you need to keep you comfortable while you wait?" I would have had a completely different perception rather than feeling abandoned in a cold room.

> ☑ **Keeping patients informed is not an easy task. It is impossible to overcommunicate. Without discipline in execution, best practices such as whiteboards and regular information updates can easily be forgotten and unused by staff. Track and reward usage of the best practices you implement.**

Service Basics

Norton Healthcare (Louisville, KY) instituted "service basics" in the fall of 2005. Their e-mail tagline says, "It begins with me," which is a very powerful statement. The brochure for the service initiative discusses respect, integrity, VIP service, and excellence in relation to patients, guests, and coworkers, with wonderful examples of each.

Our patients, guests, and coworkers know I respect them because—

- I treat others with honesty, courtesy, respect, compassion, and as if their needs were my own
- I communicate with courtesy, clarity, and respect by listening attentively, answering calls quickly and cheerfully, using good telephone etiquette, using appropriate language that is easily understood, and always saying "please" or "thank you"
- I demonstrate teamwork by treating coworkers with courtesy, respect, and professionalism; cooperate and help coworkers without being asked; share my knowledge and experience; and show consideration for others' priorities

Our patients, guests, and coworkers have faith in my professional and personal integrity because—

- I keep patients and guests informed by giving specific detailed information and instructions, educating them about our processes, procedures, and expectations, explaining and apologizing for unavoidable delays, and providing periodic updates when waiting is necessary
- I protect our patients' privacy and maintain a secure and trusting environment by discussing patient information in private, away from public areas; keep patient records and information confidential; and knock before entering a room and closing doors and curtains when appropriate
- I do the right things for patients, guests, and coworkers by complying with all applicable laws, regulations, policies, and procedures; turning

"can't" into "can" at every opportunity; and acting in the best interests of our patients, guests, employees, and physicians

Our patients, guests, and coworkers receive VIP service that makes them feel welcomed and special because—

- I use the 15/5 rule: at 15 feet, I acknowledge every guest and coworker by making eye contact; at 5 feet, I smile and greet them
- If guests appear to be lost or confused, I offer to escort them to their destination
- I provide prompt, compassionate service that exceeds expectation by understanding concerns and expectations; anticipating needs; showing concern and compassion; viewing complaints and problems as opportunities for improvement; and completing tasks accurately and in a timely manner
- I show appreciation by saying "thank you" for choosing Norton Healthcare; for their assistance and their patience; for bringing things to our attention; and for giving us their comments and feedback

Our patients, guests, and coworkers have confidence in my commitment to excellence because—

- I am always on stage making a great impression by smiling and extending a friendly greeting to all guests and coworkers; dressing appropriately for my job and maintaining a professional appearance; maintaining a clean, neat work area; helping others keep public areas such as hallways, lobbies, and waiting rooms looking nice; and adopting a helping attitude
- I demonstrate pride in Norton Healthcare and in my work by taking ownership of every problem; resolving problems in a prompt and courteous manner; referring problems to someone who can resolve them if I am unable to do so myself; following up to ensure that problems are resolved satisfactorily; and using resources wisely
- I ensure a safe environment for all by taking adequate precautions to protect patients, guests, coworkers; reporting all accidents and injuries promptly; correcting or reporting safety hazards promptly; using proper body mechanics and protective equipment when appropriate; knowing my responsibilities in emergency preparedness; and practicing preventative maintenance and reporting defects immediately

☑ **Patients and guests will feel welcomed, know you are committed to service excellence, know you have integrity, and know you are**

respectful when you adhere to the basics of service. Your facility can determine what is considered to be those basics.

Scripting and Accountability
By Laura Lindberg, MS, CPHQ, Knowledge Manager

Scripting can be a wonderful tool when you want to ensure that all patients are receiving the proper information and to improve communication between the staff and patients.[1] Unfortunately, while easy to suggest, it is very difficult to know whether staff are participating in the effort. Many facilities quickly dismiss the idea of scripting after a failed attempt. Many times, though, the scripts were not fully implemented. If only half the staff participate half the time, only one-quarter of patient interactions even have the opportunity to benefit from scripting exercises.

The old saying "what gets measured gets changed" applies to scripting as well. Facilities can do several things to monitor and evaluate scripting initiatives:

Hold Staff Accountable
- Build scripting expectations into performance evaluations
- Incorporate scripting updates and storytelling (e.g., situations in which scripting worked really well or not so well) as a standing staff meeting agenda item
- Create a script competency check-off form and evaluate each employee on a monthly basis for his or her appropriate use of scripts

Keep Scripting a Priority
- Provide peer-to-peer rewards and recognition awards for using scripts on a daily basis
- Spread internal scripting best practice stories via e-mail and the intranet and at staff meetings
- Post scores for all units for targeted survey questions (i.e., those questions that have scripts associated with them) on a weekly, monthly, or quarterly basis
- Keep laminated prompt cards on unit or create script cards to fit in pockets

---

[1]   J. Ryan and S. Wojciechowski, "More than Words . . . Rx for Scripting Challenges: Best Practice Techniques," *The Satisfaction Monitor* (Jul/Aug 2003). Available at *http://www.pressganey.com/products_services/readings_findings/satmon/article. php?article_id=99* (Accessed: November 1, 2006).

Monitor Implementation Success
- Test staff on appropriate script use by simulating a patient room and have a patient-actor create situations to cue staff members to use a particular script (e.g., service recovery, privacy, leaving the room)
- Administer written tests to staff to see whether they can recognize the scripts they are supposed to be using and when to use them
- Develop daily patient rounding questions that will signal to the manager doing the rounds whether scripted information has been made clear to the patient or resident

Reward and Recognize
- Sponsor employee picnics and award lunches
- Develop a means for peers to recognize other peers for using the scripts (e.g., peer recognition certificates redeemable for a small gift as an incentive)
- Give immediate visible and public praise to a staff member who is overheard using the scripts

Overcome Negative Reactions
- The name "scripting" carries negative connotations for many people. Consider other names that can help work around this problem—for example, "Words That Work," "Right Words at the Right Time," or "Exact Expressions"—or assign your own label
- Other people tackle negative feedback regarding scripting by addressing it head on. Point out the fact that in our clinical interactions we have prescribed behaviors. Why can't we apply the same science and rigor to our service interactions?

☑ **Scripting can be helpful to staff by reducing ambiguity and creating consistent service.**

Helping or Hindering?
By Michelle M. Gloss, MS, System Consultant

When I was working at the clinic in New Orleans, on my way back from an errand at the hospital, I saw a man in a wheelchair about one-and-a-half blocks from the clinic. The sidewalks in New Orleans were treacherous and he had gotten his wheelchair lodged in a large crack. The man was obviously a stroke victim, and the wheel he needed to turn (to free himself) was on his bad side.

Here I come to the rescue. I got his wheel unstuck and then looked at the remaining length of sidewalk between him and the bus stop (which is where I assumed he wanted to go). It was a mass of uneven pavement and overgrown with weeds, so I asked him if I could push him the rest of the way and he nodded enthusiastically. When we got to the bus stop, I parked him, said "there you go," and prepared to walk away. He managed to grab my hand and pointed toward the hospital, which was still about four or five blocks away. I asked him where he wanted to go, but he couldn't tell me (I later learned that he was aphasic, too). He just kept pointing toward the hospital.

I asked him if he needed to go to "Charity" and he nodded his head again. So off we went, down Tulane Avenue, toward the hospital. After we made it about two blocks, I heard a woman's voice yelling, "Ma'am! Ma'am!" I stopped and turned around to see a woman running toward us. As she reached us, sweating profusely and breathless, she thanked me for stopping and proceeded to tell me that the person was her uncle, who she brought to the clinic for his appointment. She left him in the waiting room while she ran some small errands and hadn't been gone for long. Apparently, her uncle took quick advantage of the opportunity to escape and I, trying to be kind, had nearly helped him escape!

We walked back to the clinic together, with her fussing at him and me wondering just how long I would have pushed him until I figured out something was amiss. The patient was obviously having a good laugh at our expense, and the story kept the clinic staff laughing for weeks. The niece told me later that we really made his day, because he was "quite a handful" when he was well, and his attempted escape made him feel almost "normal." I'm just glad she found us before we got to the French Quarter!

☑ **Sometimes presumptions are made that lead to a series of events that could have been avoided simply by obtaining more information in the initial stages. Take the time to outline the exact situation before making a determination or taking action. This will not only save time in the end, but avoid costly (or, embarrassing) mistakes.**

Communication: Sender and Receiver
By Julie Tabler, Lead Consultant

When my daughter was little, she would talk to me, and if she thought she did not have my full attention, she would place her hands on my cheeks, turn my head to face her, and ask "Mommy, are you listening to me?" Despite her young age, she knew that sometimes we just don't always listen closely.

Communication requires both a sender and a receiver. Patients won't grab our cheeks and tell us if we don't hear them or they don't understand us. We do get feedback from our patient surveys. Patient satisfaction results will tell us where we can improve and how we communicate. Consider the following common staff-patient interactions:

Meal delivery—Communication can express two entirely different attitudes: genuine concern versus "just doing a job." Go beyond just dropping food off to serving the needs of the whole person by asking the following: "Good morning, Mrs. Jones. How are you today? Is this a good time for me to bring in your breakfast? Where would you like your tray? Is there anything else I can do for you?"

Blood draws—There is a difference between being truly cared for and being treated like a piece of meat. The social taboos of the normal world, such as privacy and personal space, often are forgotten in the world of the sick. Caring can be communicated in ways such as these: "The doctor ordered for [1, or 2, or 3] vials of blood to be drawn to check if your white blood cell count is normal. Do you have a preference for which arm I draw blood? I will be placing a rubber band around the upper arm and ask you to make a fist, then you'll feel the stick. Would you like for a nurse or family member to sit with you for comfort or to squeeze your hand?"

Family waiting—Another suggestion is to have a representative of your facility stationed in the waiting areas (i.e., for the patient waiting to have a test or treatment done, waiting for the results of the test or treatment, or a family member waiting for their loved one to get out of surgery) to communicate and inform them of how much longer it is going to be and what will come next (if needed). The appointed representative is the liaison between the family and the physician or hospital. The representative is there to provide communication and comfort. Consider the following:

> "The doctor will be out in 10 minutes to speak with you. Would you like me to get you a cup of coffee while you wait?"

> "The procedure takes about 30 minutes. Why don't you go down to the cafeteria and get a bite of food. I'll come get you if there is any change."

Are you communicating in a way that the patient or family fully understands? Are you using big words, strange words, or scary words that would cause "selective hearing" or a misunderstanding? The importance of communication and the seriousness of doing it successfully was illustrated when my husband was at an important doctor's appointment. My husband has high blood pressure and high cholesterol. He's on medication to control it, but he heard the doctor say "need to take" but not the part about "every day" and "watch what you eat" or "could cause heart problems in the future." Had I not been there to provide a second set of ears, he could have made a serious mistake in taking his medications, which could have negatively affected his health.

> ☑ **What you say and how you say it matters. Take the time to analyze how you're communicating during key encounters. Consider how the patient and family could interpret what you say.**

Checklist: Communication with Nurses

The following is a checklist of proven tactics to improve patients' evaluations of communication with nurses. For more details on any item, refer to the previous stories.

- Welcome patients in a memorable fashion.
- Create standards, scripting, and training for every key patient encounter. Examples of common encounters that can be scripted include:

  - ☑ Admissions
  - ☑ Wait times
  - ☑ HIPAA
  - ☑ Introductions
  - ☑ "First Touch"
  - ☑ Tests or treatments
  - ☑ Meals
  - ☑ Cleaning the room
  - ☑ Closing the door/curtain for privacy
  - ☑ Leaving the room
  - ☑ Response to call bells
  - ☑ Drawing blood
  - ☑ Family or visitors
  - ☑ Service recovery
  - ☑ Discharge
  - ☑ Explaining the patient satisfaction survey
  - ☑ When passing others in the hall, smiling within 10 feet and saying "Hello" within 5 feet (or similar script for acknowledging others).

- Hold staff accountable to standards, keep it a priority, monitor the implementation success, and continuously reward and recognize.
- Hold fast to certain standards or rules. With some things, making no exceptions will win you the respect of teammates. Once everyone sees that you or the hospital mean business, things will begin to change.
- Use multiple mediums to ensure effective communication with patients.

- Positively reinforce the desirable behaviors. Reward and recognition not only encourages future performance, but it provides genuine satisfaction to those being recognized and rewarded. Even a simple, heartfelt "Good job!" or "Thank you *so* much!" can mean a lot.
- Reward those nurses who most fervently dedicate themselves to service with a trip to the Press Ganey annual conference. They'll be energized to continue their great work.

Chapter 2.

Responsiveness of Hospital Staff

How It's Measured

T he domain "Responsiveness of the Hospital Staff" is covered in three HCAHPS survey questions:

- ☑ During this hospital stay, after you pressed the call button, how often did you get help as soon as you wanted it?
- ☑ During this hospital stay, did you need help from nurses or other hospital staff in getting to the bathroom or in using a bedpan? Yes or No → If No, Go to Question 12 (i.e., skip the next question).
- ☑ How often did you get help in getting to the bathroom or in using a bedpan as soon as you wanted?

These two questions basically assess patients' experiences with two aspects of their stay: (1) nurse response to call lights and (2) going to the bathroom/using the bedpan. The instruction to skip the next question is designed to limit responses only to those patients who needed assistance. Patients estimate the frequency of these behaviors by selecting one of four response options: Never, Sometimes, Usually, or Always. For the call button question, an additional option is available: "I never pressed the call button."

The key to these questions is "as soon as you wanted." Patients' expectations for time lines will vary not only from patient to patient but also from moment to moment. We can all think of moments during which our sense of urgency or need was far greater than during most moments. In this sense, there is no universal, objective timeliness standard. No magic bullet or golden rule of thumb says, "If you respond in less than one minute, you'll get the highest scores." Patients don't carry stopwatches.

Responsiveness is ultimately a subjective feeling of how staff responded. That's why the information from your Press Ganey survey will help you delve into exactly what about staff members' responses need improvement. Look to your performance in questions from the Nursing and Personal Issues sections as well as patients' comments in those sections.

As with other questions, one extraordinarily negative or positive encounter may sway a patient's response to one of the extremes. This is particularly true if the patient's moment of need was great. Ultimately, it comes down to patient perceptions of timeliness and their individual standards for timeliness given their perceived intensity of need.

The Patient's Perspective

Patients often feel powerless. Unless you've been there, you probably cannot understand the intense feeling of helplessness and distress that comes with being immobilized in a hospital bed. Patients deal with this in different ways. Some ways that patients deal with this stress may lead us to label them as being "demanding" or "difficult," or to use other more negative terms to describe their behavior.

Nurses and hospital staff often remember the patients that are most difficult. The notion of categorizing patients into "good" or "bad" patients is an emotional reaction that we must resist.

We can work to improve responsiveness in two ways: (1) improving real response time and (2) improving patient perceptions of our timeliness.

Improving the actual response time is possible. We can organize care processes and standard procedures in ways that improve how quickly we get to the patient. Many factors can influence response times, such as the following: unit design and layout, nurse-patient staffing ratios, standards for who can respond to call lights, supply availability and layout, and the efficacy of supporting departments.

Improving patient perceptions is equally possible. Perceived timeliness depends upon our communication. For example, patients will perceive that we're acting in a more time-sensitive manner when we use the following communication behaviors:

- Assure the patient that we will respond in a timely fashion
- Have an understanding of how urgent the patient feels their need is
- Display a sense of urgency equal to theirs (it's best to give a sense of urgency without the patient feeling you are panicked)
- Give patients updates on requests that are complex and taking a long time
- Apologize when you fail to meet patient needs.

Service recovery can be employed when patient expectations for timeliness have not been met. Successful service recovery can smooth over the mistake and help patients "forgive" the service failure when completing their survey.

Many people ask whether answering the call light via the intercom fulfills patient perceptions or whether this occurs only when the person physically arrives in the room. This approach—determining the precise minimum work necessary—is hospital-focused and not successful. The patient-centered approach recognizes that each patient has a unique need. That need is fully met when the patient perceives that their request for help was fulfilled.

Our Stories

The 3-Foot Rule
By Laura Lindberg, MS, CPHQ, Knowledge Manager

The hallways of hospital inpatient floors are busy places. Numerous staff members beyond the nurses walk by patients' rooms every day. With this vast amount of traffic, there are many opportunities to respond to call lights. St. John's Mercy Medical (St. Louis, MO) took advantage of this traffic flow by implementing the 3-foot rule.

The 3-foot rule requires that **any** staff member within 3 feet of a patient room when a call light goes off is to respond to the light. Answering the call light takes precedence over anything that is not a matter of life and death. This applies to housekeeping, dietary, nurses, maintenance, administration, and so on. If the respondent is able to fulfill the request, they immediately do it. Requests that are clinical in nature are turned over to the appropriate nurse. By using whiteboards in the room that have the nurse's name, the staff member can personally find that nurse and convey the request. The respondent's responsibility is not fulfilled until the request has been filled or it has been accepted by another staff member. If the request is passed on, the respondent is encouraged to follow up with the patient to make sure it was fulfilled to their satisfaction.

Responding to call lights is the responsibility of all staff. The 3-foot rule empowers all staff to ensure that all patient needs are being met.

☑ **Not all call button requests are clinical in nature. It is the responsibility of all staff to respond to patient requests.**

Everyone Answers Call Lights
By Jodie Cunningham, Solutions Consultant

Albert Einstein Healthcare Network (Philadelphia, PA) trained all their staff (both clinical and nonclinical) to respond to call lights. To make their program a success, they obtained buy-in from the nurse manager on the unit. They trained all nonclinical staff in the unit on scripting, protocols, and intercom usage. All staff were scripted to end interactions with "I am available to help you now, is there anything else I can do for you? If not, I will return in __ minutes." The caregivers were responsible for updating the dry-erase boards in the patient room to provide the name of the contact person for nonclinical staff to reference. Flyers were placed on the unit to remind all staff of their responsibility to answer calls. The nurse manager rounded on patients to assess the program and compliance. Finally, after completing implementation, they celebrated their success.

> ☑ **All staff can be trained to answer call lights, reducing the burden on nursing staff and providing timely attention to patients. To be successful you need to obtain buy-in on the unit and develop a clear response plan.**

Service Beyond Expectations

"Together we create a caring experience by taking pride in providing service beyond expectations." This is W.A. Foote Memorial Hospital's description of customer service, a core value of Foote Health System that is deeply held by the entire staff.

As with other health systems, the challenge has been to transform this value into bottom-line results. The keys to achieving this goal were organizational alignment and the relentless pursuit of best practices.

Two years ago, Foote Health System's overall inpatient satisfaction score was at the 22nd percentile compared to its peers. While most patients were giving "good" ratings, the system had a long way to go toward becoming a top performer.

As part of the organization's planning process, service excellence was made a strategic priority and specific improvement targets were identified. Next, the organization-wide goals were broken down into department-specific performance improvement plans and then into individual commitment statements.

Best practices guided the action planning. The team read many books and articles, attended conferences, spoke with high performers, and eventually engaged a coach. Consequently, the organization was able to zero in on the four tactics that most significantly improve the customer experience:

Hourly Rounds—Caregivers make rounds with their patients every hour to assess the "Three Ps" (Pain, Potty, and Position). They also make sure that necessary objects are within the patient's reach, and they always end the visit by asking, "Is there anything else I can do for you? I will be back in an hour, and here is the call light in case you need anything before I return."

Individualized Care—During admission, patients are asked what "very good care" means to them. Their responses are recorded on a white board for everyone to see. Throughout the patient's stay, all caregivers refer to this board and use it as a guide. For example, a physician responded to a patient's desire for a daily milkshake by bringing one with him on his rounding visit.

Response to Call Lights—The staff is expected to respond to call lights within two minutes. As a result, patients now rate "promptness in responding to call lights" above the 70th percentile.

Discharge Phone Calls—Every patient is contacted by phone within a few days of discharge. Patients have said that they highly value these follow-up conversations with their caregivers, and the calls have the added benefit of providing an opportunity to gather feedback on staff.

As the journey toward service excellence continues, Foote is focused on "hard-wiring" that culture throughout the entire health system. This means that customer service is no longer optional, it is now part of the culture.

All departments are united in the pursuit of a common goal. Staff members participate on customer service teams to help them embrace the new direction. Leaders are expected to coach and mentor their staff members, helping develop the skills needed to provide excellent customer service. Leaders no longer hesitate to use corrective action for poor customer service. By setting and reinforcing high standards, Foote Health System has created a passion for excellence that will carry the organization into the future.

> ☑ **Our expectations for service have increased over the years. Customizing care to meet each individual's unique needs enables the ability to exceed expectations.**

Patients Know Their Bodies
By A Patient

During a two-week hospitalization, I was given some medication to help me sleep. The nurses perceived that I was having problems sleeping because I was up until one or two in the morning most nights. When asked if I was having trouble sleeping, I replied that I was not—I was just a night owl, which was exacerbated by frequent naps during the day. Apparently, the nurse was not convinced. As she explained each one of my evening pills, she showed me a new one that would help me sleep. I asked about it because I am highly sensitive to the effects of narcotics and even refused pain medication during most of my stay. I was told that it was just a little dose and that it would help relax me. Later that night, I had a horrible nightmare and when I woke up, it was still there. Eventually, I was able to press the call button for the night nurse. When he asked me what was wrong, I whispered that there was a monster in my room at the foot of my bed, glaring at me. He immediately pulled my chart and said, "No more sleeping pills for you. Wow—and that was a little one, too." If everyone had simply listened to me from the beginning, I would have been spared this experience.

Another experience occurred in an ED. I crashed on my mountain bike and suffered a spiral fracture of my fibula. The fracture was painful, but not unbearable, so when I wasn't offered pain medication at any time during my stay in the ED, I didn't complain. Just as I was preparing to leave, a nurse approached me with a syringe. I asked him what it was for and he informed me it was a pain shot. I let him know that I was very sensitive to pain medication and that a "normal" dose would be too much for me. He said that he was sure that the dose he prepared was fine and gave me the shot. Minutes later, as I stood reviewing discharge instructions with the nurse, I suddenly said, "I'm going to be sick," which was followed seconds later by my saying, "I'm going to pass out." They lifted me back up on the exam table until I felt better, which was 30 minutes later—a costly delay in a busy ED.

In both situations, I could have refused the medication completely; however, in both cases, I informed the clinical staff of my sensitivity and was assured no harm would come to me. It seemed like further discussion about the matter would have been argumentative and I was, after all, a patient.

> ☑ **Patients know themselves. It's not enough just to ask for their input;** *listen* **to what they say and believe them.**

Responding More Effectively
By Jodie Cunningham, Solutions Consultant

Several actions can ensure quick responses to patients' call bells. First, analyze the times when calls are most frequent. One Press Ganey client discovered that many of their calls came during the 30 minutes after tray delivery/meal time. They decided that they would no longer allow the nurses to take breaks during that 30 minutes and instead they would be available. Another consideration is how you respond. Patients are generally more satisfied when you respond in person instead of via an intercom. If you must use your intercom, you should have a system in place to respond to those patients who have difficulty hearing or are uncomfortable using the intercom system. Finally, developing a program in which all staff must respond to call lights can provide assistance to your nursing staff.

> ☑ **Analyzing your call button "busy times" and taking appropriate steps to improve how the staff handles that time can go a long way toward improving patient satisfaction.**

A Commode for You!
By A Patient

I spent my freshman year spring break in Memphis, Tennessee, with a group of my friends. After our 13-hour drive back to Ames, Iowa, I started to feel sick. We drove to the grocery store to pick up something for dinner, but I just grabbed a can of soup. I gave myself insulin and started cooking my dinner. I soon found out that I was not going to be able to eat any food.

For most people, not being able to eat would not be fun, but they would survive. For a diabetic who had already taken her insulin, this was bad. My blood sugars had started going down to dangerous levels and I could not keep any juice or pop down to get my sugars back up. It was determined I needed to go to the closest ED.

I was quickly taken back into a large single-room ED and hooked up on IV glucose. Once my blood sugars were stabilized, I was examined for the pain in my stomach. Blood was drawn to get my white blood cell count, and we found out it was extremely high. The doctor felt one possible cause for my pain was a urinary tract infection. I tried to convince him that that was not the problem, to no avail.

The doctor walked out of my little curtained area and let me know he would need a urine sample. Up until now, things had been going along just fine. The next thing I saw was the nurse rolling in a commode for me to use. Note that the curtain around me ended about 3 feet off of the floor—just about level with the commode seat. I quickly realized giving a sample was not going to be as easy as the doctor and nurse indicated it should be.

I sat on the bed looking at the commode and listening to the woman on the bed 5 feet from me moaning from her liver infection. (This illustrates the lack of privacy; I should not know this woman's medical details.) The nurse returned and I did not have anything to give her. I asked for some water. After consulting with the doctor, the nurse returned with a little Dixie® cup of water for me. Again, I had a sinking feeling about my situation.

The second time the nurse returned, I asked if I could use a bathroom. I was told no and brought another two ounces of water in another Dixie cup. The third time the nurse returned, I was threatened with a catheter. The nurse's exact words were, "If you can't give me a sample, I am going to have to go in and take one. You really won't like that."

Mortified, I asked—no pleaded—to use a bathroom instead of the exposed commode that was rolled up to me. A little frustrated, the nurse left to talk with the doctor again. To my relief, the nurse pulled the curtains back and tersely stated, "Follow me." To everyone else's relief, a little privacy was all that I needed!

☑ **A little privacy makes a whole lot of difference. Think about how your interactions can enhance the sense of privacy.**

Service Recovery: Is It Being Used?
By Beth Heck, Regional Service Manager

I was working at an academic teaching hospital in the South to meet with every manager and a good portion of the staff to help them in their patient satisfaction improvement efforts. We conducted multiple separate sessions for each service line. Before heading to the hospital, I spoke with my contact about their service recovery program. We discussed the importance of having a good program in place. She let me know they had that covered. She outlined their entire process and explained all the steps to me, and I went in with a great idea of how their program was working.

In each session, I asked who was using the service recovery program. No more than one-third of the staff knew that a service recovery program even existed. Probing further, less than half of those who knew of the program actually followed the process outlined by the contact.

Afterward, I discussed what I learned with the contact. It turned out that my contact and her supervisor created the service recovery program, posted the information on their intranet, and believed that was all that was needed. They missed the most critical step—changing staff behavior. To have an impact on patient experience, you've got to change the creation of that experience—that is, the interaction between staff and patient. In other words, the challenge is changing the behavior of hundreds or thousands of staff members. A post on the intranet Web site will not successfully change the behavior of your entire hospital staff.

Particularly for service recovery programs, staff must know about the program before they take advantage of the program and handle complaints differently. Changing behavior requires acceptance (i.e., buy-in) by the person whose behavior you'd like to change. Involving staff in the creation of the program will significantly increase the adoption of those behaviors. Educating and involving staff makes it easier to encourage accountability to follow the procedures at all times.

Ask hospital staff for their ideas to contribute to the program: they know their patients, their unit, and what will work. Hold training sessions for the new programs that involve practice and role-play, so that it gives staff a safe place to try new behaviors. Initiatives like service recovery require evangelism—spread the word and convert your staff!

☑ **The success of most service initiatives depends on staff changing their behavior. Track what percentage of staff know and practice** your desired behaviors. Take proactive steps to ensure that your program(s) is not only communicated, but communicated well.

Service Recovery: Emory Healthcare System
By Renee Doren, MBA, System Consultant

Emory Healthcare System (Atlanta, GA) implemented "scripts for improvement," particularly for use in their environmental services and facilities departments.

The environmental service staff member leaves a card in every patient room. The card lets them know who prepared and cleaned the room for their comfort. The card also lets the patient know staff checked to ensure that all necessary equipment was in working order before their arrival. If the patient sees a need to have something taken care of in the room, they can refer to the card and call the number printed on it.

The telephone number for patients or staff is monitored 24/7 and resolution to all concerns and complaints are tracked in a database. The goal set was to have 100 percent resolution to calls in 30 minutes or less. Staff handles all complaints as a work order, but if no actual work is required, they look at the call as an opportunity to improve customer service and to connect with their patients.

The department created a song that they sing when leadership attends any of their meetings. The last verse of the song really brings home their passion and the message. The verse states, "It's so amazing the change that occurs, when we treat our patients like our family."

The efforts of this department can truly be attested to—just read these two comments from two different patient surveys: "The room is always clean and everything works" and "The room was clean, fresh, and the person who cleaned the room was friendly and polite" (comments from actual patient surveys).

> ☑ **Focus clinical staff on improving their communication, interaction, clinical duties, and service to patients. Get ancillary departments to join in practicing prompt service recovery responses regarding cleanliness, maintenance, and equipment repairs. Connect them directly with the patients to ensure timely resolution. This leaves the patient and visitors with a perception of their overall care being attended to, while leaving the clinical staff to use their time doing what they were trained to do.**

Taking the Patient Experience to the Next Level

Seven miles north of the US/Mexico border is Sharp Chula Vista Medical Center (Chula Vista, CA) with 1,400 employees, 230 general acute care beds, and 100 skilled nursing beds. In October 2001, Sharp Chula Vista Medical

Center joined the entire Sharp HealthCare system in launching "The Sharp Experience," a strategic initiative to become the best hospital for employees to work, physicians to practice medicine, and patients to receive care.

By December 2002, Sharp Chula Vista had made little progress toward breaking out of the lower quartile of the Press Ganey national Inpatient database. The facility faced many challenges:

- While unit staff supported "The Sharp Experience," not all staff had opportunities to take ownership of the process.
- Staff didn't clearly understand satisfaction goals or get regular progress updates.
- Patients received little information about satisfaction goals or the survey process.
- Hospital leadership dealt with conflicting priorities that prevented them from focusing on the strategies with the greatest impact on patient satisfaction.
- Unit leaders had difficulty completing daily rounds on patients.

Sharp Chula Vista took a series of important steps to overcome its challenges and accomplish its objectives:

- Service imperatives were clarified. We focused on three areas that would have the most impact on overall patient satisfaction: 1) pain control, 2) meeting special/personal needs, and 3) prompt call-light response.
- Nursing assistants were given the sole job of meeting patients' personal needs, which also helped reduce the number of call lights. The CNO established training to improve skill levels and confidence in this area.
- Nursing units use cell phones and a "must respond" approach to facilitate prompt call-light response.
- Existing processes for pain control are emphasized. Individual units use a variety of scripts and other techniques to meet this core component of patient care.
- Managers and leads round on every shift every day. They discuss care given by staff, their overall satisfaction, identify issues that need attention, recognize positive staff behaviors, and review the survey process. Use of rounding logs is enforced by the CNO.
- Inpatients receive a thank you note signed by staff and a post-discharge phone call from a nurse. The process also serves to remind patients about the satisfaction survey.
- Weekly reports trending patient satisfaction are posted and discussed with staff. Survey images are also posted in each unit. Patient satisfaction goals are part of annual evaluations.

- Hospital-wide satisfaction action-teams were decentralized to the unit level to promote ownership and accountability.
- Intensive training on the "how-tos" of rounding provided to charge nurses, supervisors, leads, and managers.
- The CEO sends a weekly e-mail to staff addressing satisfaction priorities and recognizing high performers for that week. The CNO holds regular meetings with clinical managers to discuss progress and barriers to satisfaction. Patient satisfaction is a standing item at the weekly executive team meeting and monthly hospital leadership meetings.

Sharp Chula Vista Medical Center increased its overall patient satisfaction rating in one year from a mean of 81.3 to 85.0, a difference of +3.7 mean points. As a result, they were awarded the annual *Compass Award* from Press Ganey for being one of the most improved inpatient facilities in the nation.

> ☑ **Sustained improvement is not made with one quick hit or one person. It results from dozens of initiatives and the individual actions of caregivers to adopt each initiative into their daily routine with patients.**

Put Yourself in Their Shoes
By Beth Heck, Regional Service Manager

When asked, most employees will tell you they work in health care because they like helping people. On a daily basis, however, it is easy to forget that main reason for doing the job they do. Staff can easily fall into the same day-to-day routines and no longer see the patients as individuals but rather as another task to accomplish.

As staff fall into this routine they tend to resist the topic of patient satisfaction. Many employees do not see how the patients perceive their daily routines. The top priority items for hospitals across the country are always issues that have to do with the personal attention a patient is given by staff. If employees are not aware of how patients view their attitudes and actions, it will be hard to excel in these areas.

There are ways to help combat this issue and help the staff learn that every detail of their interactions with the patient is important to the person's overall satisfaction. Many facilities have implemented programs for staff to learn great customer service skills. For example, Floyd Medical Center (Rome, GA) implemented an interactive four-day training program for all staff called Camp Floyd. The first part of this program revolves around employee orientation; every new employee goes through one day of training dedicated to customer service. All full-time staff participates in the four-day training, and each day has a different focus, which all pertain to how they view service through the patient's eyes.

Many different parts of the Camp Floyd method can be used to work with staff to give them the patient's perspective. Skits and role-playing can be one of the most effective ways to get a point across to staff. At Camp Floyd, they use cutouts of nine "patients" who share their story with staff. These are real examples of patient stories and experiences with staff. Other facilities have used skits of real-life scenarios to help educate staff. To do this, they found willing participants and created skits with two outcomes: one negative and one positive. After the skits were completed, the staff was asked to identify what the people in the skits could have done better. When employees see these skits, the hope is that they will give more thought to the daily actions that they normally wouldn't think twice about. This is a great opportunity for staff to internally evaluate their own performance.

Many hospitals I have worked with have succeeded in helping staff see themselves through the eyes of the patient. Some of the best ways include the following:

- *Sharing real-life patient stories.* Facilities receive patient stories on a daily basis, both good and bad. Telling these stories—either through patient letters or bringing in former patients—helps spur improvement ideas. Doing this on a regular schedule keeps patient perceptions at the forefront.
- *In-house training videos.* Many facilities write, act out, and film skits, such as those mentioned above. These skits typically feature different common service scenarios, such as waiting in the emergency room (ER), patient transport, and a day in the life of a patient. The approaches vary from worst-case to best-case scenarios, demonstrate a service standard or new process, or reenact true events. Engaging staff or senior administrators in the roles creates a buzz around the video—it gets people excited and talking about it. Most find viewing in small groups the most successful method, because it allows for more discussion and interaction. Plus, these videos serve as great resources to be used over and over again.
- *Distribute solution starters from eCompass.* For every question on the survey, there is a definition given through the eyes of the patient. Use these definitions at staff meetings: pick one question, discuss the definition from the patient's perspective, give good or bad examples of staff and patient stories relating to the question, and ask staff what roadblocks they may face. Have staff give ideas about how they can excel in these areas.
- *Patient comments.* Qualitative data are just as valuable as quantitative data. Patients will identify specific problems in their survey comments. The best-performing hospitals disseminate all comments out to the

respective units or departments and have teams in place to rapidly rectify the cause of every negative patient comment.

For high patient satisfaction, understanding how patients perceive their care is imperative. Achieving this insight among all staff may seem insurmountable, but it can be achieved with time and creativity.

> ☑ **Staff need to have an understanding of how patients perceive the care they are given to truly be able to improve the customer service they are giving.**

Employee Empowerment
By Linda Paustian, System Consultant

I visited a client's very busy emergency department in Wuesthoff Hospital (Rockledge, FL). My host, the patient satisfaction coordinator, walked me around the redesigned area with state-of-the-art patient monitoring and tracking information systems.

Suddenly, someone called for help. Without hesitation, my host immediately went into the ER examining room. She asked the patient what was needed. The patient wanted some ice water. The employee contacted the charge nurse to see if the patient could have some ice water. Upon receiving the confirmation it was okay, she filled a large cup with water, asked the patient if she'd like a straw, and positioned the cup to an optimal position for the patient. Later, my host followed up with the charge nurse to let her know that she had given the patient water.

In the course of the day, this was a little thing to my host, but it made a difference to the patient and to the swamped nurses working that shift.

> ☑ **Employee empowerment means total ownership of service issues. Successfully empowered environments feature:**
> > **(a) Managers promoting empowerment by actually giving associates autonomy, and**
> > **(b) Employees accepting and adopting an ownership attitude.**

Investigating the Reasons for Call Bells
By A Press Ganey Client

A client shared this research project with us on the condition of anonymity. They sought to ascertain why patients used the call bell. By understanding why patients used it, they could determine how to change the system to improve patient satisfaction. You can replicate this study at your own facility, if you're interested in testing the results yourself. Following is a synopsis of the project from the hospital's perspective.

Background: The hospital is a 700-plus-bed tertiary care, trauma receiving, suburban hospital and part of a larger health system. They have been a Press Ganey member for five quarters and have realized that measurement does not impact scores, action impacts scores.

Purpose: After reading and distributing copies of *Patient Satisfaction* by Irwin Press, they understood why their scores had remained generally flat; they needed to look behind the indicator to what the patient was actually experiencing. Senior management and the CEO of the institution selected a staff member trained in the Six Sigma Methodology for data collection to look at a "simple" Press Ganey indicator.

Area for Investigation: There was a need to find out why their patients were so dissatisfied with their call bell service. The indicator reads "Promptness of Response to Call." First, there was a need to understand patient expectations. A survey was conducted of 50 patients on two general medicine floors. This helped identify the time frame for "Promptness." Then the patients were asked what they expected would happen when the call bell was answered. This allowed for a map of the complete process from the patient's point of view. It identified the start and end of this indicator. The results showed that the bell was perceived to have been answered promptly if the staff arrived in the room and the patient was able to obtain the information, assistance, or requested item by the end of the encounter, which would lead to satisfaction.

What the Data Showed: Data were collected over one week (all inclusive, 24/7) on a single general medicine floor. Collection points were the ring of the bell to the answer at the desk, the message relay to staff, the reported reason and real reason for the call, and time until satisfaction. The data surprised everyone. Many staff had guessed that patients were ringing for issues of emotional "handholding," such as "fluff my pillow," or that family were "using the bell to get the nurse to tell her something about the patient." But the data showed something different. The number one reason for ringing bells (31.7 percent, $n=220$) was that the patients were in pain. The number two reason (27 percent, $n=220$) was for IV beeping, which was followed by bathroom requests and general assistance needed. These indicators are both important medically and emotionally to the patient.

☑ **Chances are, the call light went on for a very good reason. Most patients don't demand "pillow-fluffing."**

Rules Are Made to Be Broken
By Melissa Thatcher, System Consultant

Before giving a presentation to a group of nearly 100 hospital senior leaders and managers, the CEO told his staff an inspirational story. A woman was admitted to the hospital and wanted to talk to her family—certainly not out of the ordinary—except her family lived in Sweden. Her physician indicated that her stay might not be a short one. The hospital did not allow patients to make international phone calls, but if she was not able to call her family, it could be several weeks before she was able to talk to them.

Her nurse decided there must be a way for this woman to communicate with her family, even though "the rules" did not allow for international calls. The nurse called her supervisor and after several more calls, the issue made its way to the CEO who said, "Let's make this happen," and they did!

When the CEO finished his story, he explained that this was just the kind of outside-the-box thinking that would help meet the individual needs of their patients. He challenged his staff to recognize that each patient and their family will have different needs and that they cannot say, "that's just how we do it." They must continually find new and innovative ways to help their patients.

> ☑ We know "the rules" are there for a reason, but sometimes they need to be broken. To meet patient needs, sometimes we have to challenge the rules.

Checklist: Responsiveness

The following is a checklist of proven tactics to improve the perceived responsiveness of hospital staff. For more details on any item, refer to the previous stories.

- Start an organization-wide service recovery program. Conduct an annual training for all staff. Track usage. If units aren't using it, there is something amiss.
- Round on patients—*hourly* for unit staff, daily for nurse managers and leaders.
- Create an ownership culture.
- Empower employees to do whatever is necessary to meet patients' needs.
- Respect patients by acknowledging their awareness of their own bodies. Trust that they're competent until proven otherwise.
- Conduct your own QI project investigating reasons for your current performance in call light related issues. It may be an issue of timeliness, but it may also be an issue of *what happens* when someone responds.

- Education, training, and practice are the keys to honing communication skills.

  - ☑ Practice with each other. In trainings, team meetings, and at home.
  - ☑ Share real-life patient stories. Discuss different ways to address an issue.
  - ☑ Create your own training videos.

- Leaders must walk the talk. Fortunately, anyone can be a leader—not just those with the title. Exemplify the behaviors you want your fellow staff members to emulate.

Chapter 3.

Communication with Doctors

How It's Measured

The domain "Communication with Doctors" is covered in three HCAHPS survey questions:

- ☑ During this hospital stay, how often did doctors treat you with <u>courtesy and respect?</u>
- ☑ During this hospital stay, how often did doctors <u>listen carefully to you?</u>
- ☑ During this hospital stay, how often did doctors <u>explain things</u> in a way you could understand?

Patients estimate the frequency of these behaviors by selecting one of four response options: Never, Sometimes, Usually, or Always.

As mentioned previously, patients aren't spending their hospital stay with a scorecard in hand, marking down the frequency of these behaviors. Their responses depend on perception and memory recall. The underlined portions of the sentence are designed to focus patients' memories on those elements: courtesy and respect, listening carefully, and explaining things. One extraordinarily negative or positive encounter may sway their response to one of the extremes.

The Patient's Perspective

Patients value communication with their doctor, particularly after surgical procedures. Today, for planned elective procedures, patients typically don't see their admitting physician. Often, they will see multiple doctors during their stay—specialists or hospitalists—but may be disappointed by not seeing "their" doctor. This can be a challenge. Work needs to be conducted in coordination with the physician or their office to create procedures that set patients' expectations appropriately (i.e., whether the physician will see them in the hospital and, if not, why not and where or how they can get in touch with their physician, if needed).

Doctors often have less time than nurses and may be more challenged with the nuances of interpersonal communication. Additionally, dealing with the medical staff and achieving physician buy-in can be a difficult charge for hospital leaders. Our best-performing clients have learned several lessons for tackling these issues:

- Provide physician-specific scores. Physicians will often listen only to the data that directly apply to them. By showing physicians where their individual weaknesses lie, they know what they need to work on.
- Anonymously publish the provider-specific scores. Physician buy-in often comes after seeing that there is substantial variability in scores among physicians. Peer pressure is probably the biggest motivator for physician behavior change.
- Identify a physician champion. Arm them with whatever they need to lead the charge.
- Provide all physicians with business cards that have the hospital logo. Physicians, especially specialists, should begin encounters by introducing themselves to patients and family and giving them their business card. This actually benefits the physicians as well as the patient, because it promotes their services through positive word-of-mouth.
- Put stools in all patient rooms to encourage physicians to sit next to patients.
- Offer physicians free continuing medical education or training in empathy and communication skills through organizations such as the Institute for Healthcare Communication.[2]
- When a physician is positively mentioned on a survey, write a thank you note to the doctor and include a copy of the survey highlighting the actual comment. This makes the survey results seem "real" and positively reinforces desired behavior.
- Follow best practice—compile all the essential information your physicians need or typically want to know into one document, summarizing your organization's approach to patient satisfaction, employee satisfaction, physician satisfaction, quality improvement, the role you expect physicians to play, and how they will benefit.

---

[2] Institute for Healthcare Communication. Available at *http://www.healthcarecomm. org* (Accessed November 12, 2006).

The undeniable fact remains that actions speak louder than words. Proving to physicians you can make a positive impact on their patients in a way that seeks and respects their autonomy, will go a long way toward establishing your reputation for driving service excellence.

Our Stories

Can You E-Mail Your Doctor?
By Jodie Cunningham, Solutions Consultant

Kaiser Permanente now allows their enrollees to e-mail their physician for free.[3] They can send non-urgent questions and receive a reply within two business days. The communication becomes part of the patient's permanent record.

The online service allows patients to request prescription refills, schedule appointments with a primary care physician (PCP), change or cancel appointments, view some lab results, and choose or change a PCP.

> ☑ **New technology allows patients more control over their appointments, records, and physician access. This technology could assist with tracking patient defection from a practice.**

Great Hospitalist Programs
By Katie Drevs, System Consultant

Successful programs educate patients up front—patients want to know what a hospitalist is, what they can do, and that their admitting doctor will still be involved in their care. Press Ganey Success Story Winner St. John's Mercy Medical Center (St. Louis, MO) covers this by providing a brochure to patients through the physician offices and preadmission process. Other proven methods for developing successful hospitalist programs include the following:

- Set hospitalists up for success beginning in the physician office. To help hospitals prepare for unique patient conditions, successful hospitalist programs will work with physician offices to obtain regular advance notices of complex cases.
- For physicians who consistently work with a unit, set standards for the physician and staff. What method of communication does the physician prefer? What information does the physician need and not need?

---

3   C. Rauber, "Kaiser to Enrollees: Email Your Doctor," *San Francisco Business Times*, November 16, 2005.

Successful programs even customized Situation Background Assessment and Recommendations (SBARs)[4] for different physicians.

- Hold monthly or quarterly meetings with physicians to ensure that processes meet their needs and their patients' needs.
- Hold a yearly awards ceremony such as "The Oscars" and celebrate doctors. Hospital staff vote on categories such as Friendliest Doctor, Best Looking, Best Bedside Manner, Best Comedian, and so on. Outreach programs that promote teamwork improve the relationships among the staff, physicians, and patients.

☑ **Hospitalists can create huge win-win situations for hospitals, medical staff, and patients. It's worth your time to analyze what you can do to make the program successful in your area.**

Proven Patient-Physician Communication Techniques
By Jodie Cunningham, Solutions Consultant

Good interpersonal communication increases patient satisfaction with physicians. The good news is that the following techniques are easily learned:[5]

- Greet each patient with a smile, eye contact, and an introduction, addressing patient by name
- Sit down when speaking with patients
- Focus on listening skills and empathy by—
  - o Asking open-ended questions
  - o Watching for nonverbal cues
  - o Restating to patients what they told you in your own words (e.g., "So what you're telling me . . .")
- Allow patients to tell their stories without interruption. It helps you—
  - o Uncover patient's needs
  - o Discover how the problem affects their day-to-day life

---

[4] Growing in popularity, this effective practice enhances nurse-physician relationships and effectiveness by providing a standard approach to the communication. Learn more about it at *http://www.ihi.org/IHI/Topics/PatientSafety/SafetyGeneral/Tools/ SBARTechniqueforCommunicationASituationalBriefingModel.htm* (Accessed November 11, 2006).

[5] Laurence Savett, *The Human Side of Medicine: Learning what it's like to be a patient and what it's like to be a physician* (Westport: Auburn House, 2002); Scott Diering, *Love Your Patients!* (Nevada City: Blue Dolphin Press, 2004); J. Tongue, H. Epps, and L. Forese, "Communication Skills for Patient-Centered Care," *Journal of Bone and Joint Surgery* 87-A (2005): 652-58.

- Inquire about the patient's understanding of the disease or treatment. Ask for their thoughts about how this happened (i.e., soliciting the patient's explanatory model).
- Anticipate and address common concerns
- Avoid technical language
- Use keywords from the survey
- Talk up hospital staff
- Encourage patient to write down questions
- Provide contact information

> ☑ **Support your physicians' growth and ability to deliver high-quality interpersonal care by offering training and educational opportunities to learn these skills.**

EMR—Don't Let Technology Turn You Into a Robot!
By Laura Duman, System Consultant

Twenty-five brand new computer workstations with flat screen monitors, eight new printers, three new scanners, and two barcode readers . . . The office resembled the Star Ship Enterprise more and more every day. Staff were trained, doctors were onboard, plans and procedures were in place. You could feel the bustle of excitement as the first patient entered the room. After nearly a year of planning, this was it, our first day with Electronic Medical Records (EMR). The patient checked in, the patient was seen, the patient checked out. Things happened like clockwork. Finally, it seemed, all those overtime hours had paid off. The receptionist proudly asked the woman, "What do you think of all this high-tech stuff? It is pretty neat isn't it?" The woman responded, "The nurse and the doctor never looked at me; they stared at that stupid screen the entire time."

We quickly realized that technology cannot replace the comfort and understanding given with human acknowledgment, eye contact, and a smile. Patients come in because they are sick. They want to feel better. They want empathy. They want to be understood. They trust us with their lives. Our approach to technology is often provider-focused, not patient-focused. Technology can be applied to make our jobs easier, but we can apply it in a way that reassures and involves patients. Technology should supplement, not replace, good service and human interaction.

This can be accomplished in many ways, including, for example, the following:

- When introducing a technology, inform patients of the benefits. This is particularly important if the new technology forces them to do something new or different. Using the EMR example, you can tell them how, if they have to go to the ER, all of their information is readily available even if their physician is not. Tell them that it can pick up adverse drug reactions and allergies. Let them know that it will help to get them home faster because as soon as you hit "save," their prescriptions will print out at the pharmacy of their choice.

- Involve them in the process of their care. Turn the computer screen toward them and show them the graph that shows trends in their cholesterol levels for the past two years and ask them whether their life habits reflect those different fluctuations. Print out the graph and let them take it home.

- "Communication is the medium through which we deliver all care."[6] A medical facility is not a relaxing place—how we talk with patients will either put them at ease or exacerbate their stress. Examine your common verbal phrases and nonverbal behaviors to determine whether they are stress reducing or inducing. Show your human side instead of just your back side as you are turned away pointing and clicking on a computer.

- Dr. Beth Lown, Assistant Professor of Medicine at Harvard Medical School, said, "Patient satisfaction goes to the heart of medicine—the skillful enactment of communication and a truly heartfelt understanding of the patient's circumstances. And it seems to have gotten lost as doctors get involved in medical systems that prioritize speed and technology. Increasingly, people are relying on tests instead of talking to patients."[7] Eliciting the patient's explanatory model improves the accuracy of diagnosis and treatment. Ask the patient for their beliefs and thoughts regarding the cause of their illness. Asking the simple question, "What do you think could have caused this?" can open up a bevy of clinically relevant information regarding the patient's background, health behaviors, and beliefs. This can inform both diagnosis and determination of appropriate treatment.

Electronic medical records are just one example of the increasing prevalence of technology in health care. Combining the advantages of our technology age with your compassionate human spirit enables exponentially better patient care than ever before. Just don't let technology turn you into a robot!

    ☑ **Use technology to reassure and involve patients. Ensure that technology is only a supplement to and not a replacement for good service and human interaction.**

---

6   I. Press, *Patient Satisfaction: Defining, Measuring, and Improving the Experience of Care*, 2nd ed. (Chicago, IL: ACHE Press, 2005).

7   G. Kolata, "When the Doctor Is In, but You Wish He Wasn't," *New York Times*, November 30, 2005.

Quiet, I Just Might Kill Your Daughter
By David Truax, Regional Service Manager

Away from home, on vacation in the Great Smoky Mountains, our one-year-old daughter suddenly became violently ill. Irritability, diarrhea, and escalating fever made sleep impossible. At the nearest ER, helpful staff completed our registration and moved us to a treatment room within minutes. The unexplained fever reached a frightening 104 degrees. Despite our fear, the quick ER team's rapid response and courtesy made us thankful and confident. Our opinion would soon change.

Enter the physician. To reduce the fever, he paged through a small pocket guide for a pharmaceutical solution. This search was disconcerting, so we asked what he was looking for. Curtly, the physician replied, "It would be best to keep your mouths shut while I read, otherwise you might get the wrong medication or dosage and that could kill your daughter."

Although the physician selected a medication that reduced the fever and returned our daughter to her healthy and joyful self, the offhand statement regarding "killing our daughter" was rude, crude, and totally unacceptable. This one statement overshadowed everything else done and in our minds changed our ER experience from a 5 to a 1.

Reflecting on the experience, the physician probably perceived us as nervous parents asking too many questions—but this could have been handled differently. Excusing himself, he could have left the room for a moment of private concentration. He could have asked a nurse to escort us to a waiting room. His request for silence could have been communicated in a reassuring fashion, such as, "I promise I'll answer all your questions, but I need to concentrate for a moment." Instead, one sentence changed our impression of the hospital and its ER forever.

☑ **Insensitive communication can break an otherwise exceptionally positive experience.**

Have a Seat!
By Dave Trowbridge, Service Quality Specialist

Visiting my grandmother in the hospital, I was especially interested in how her doctor and nurses were caring for her. She mentioned that some were nice, while others were mean. What made someone "nice"? The "nice" staff members pulled a chair up to the side of her bed and took the time to answer her questions. She mentioned that the "mean" people also answered all of the questions she had, but they made her feel uncomfortable by towering over her. It doesn't sound like the news the "nice" ones delivered was any better than the news the "mean" people told her, but it was *how* they presented the news that mattered.

My grandmother experienced what several research studies have shown—sitting down next to the patient improves patient satisfaction, enhances communication effectiveness, and reduces anxiety.

> ☑ **Sit down next to the patient. It will help make the patient feel more relaxed and it will also allow you a few moments off your feet.**

Just Another Lung
By A Patient

With a dad who died of lung cancer and two tests—a chest X-ray and CT—revealing newfound nodules, I was anxious to see the pulmonologist. After two sleepless nights, the pulmonologist's office informed me that my appointment would not be scheduled for four weeks. When you're scared about the prospect of cancer, four weeks seems like a very long time.

Unmoved by my pleas for an earlier appointment, the staff simply repeated the doctor's education and experience to justify the appointment time. Requests to speak to the pulmonologist were refused. They were willing to give him a message but could not promise a return phone call.

With stress so intense that it affected my diabetic control and sleep, I called on my PCP to intervene. The PCP returned calls promptly and was able to negotiate an appointment in one and a half weeks. He informed me of all the factors that determined my initial appointment time (age, lack of smoking, geographic area, and lack of symptoms) and that this meant I had a relatively low likelihood of actually having lung cancer. This background information greatly eased my fears. Helping me understand why made a difference.

Although I remained somewhat stressed until the results arrived, a little compassion for my situation truly helped ease my anxiety. My pulmonologist's office may see hundreds of these cases, but this was my first time and I was scared.

> ☑ **Patients may not have ever seen any of the things you see on a daily basis. They are scared. Information and compassion easily eases these fears.**

Physician Communication
By Jodie Cunningham, Solutions Consultant

My consulting engagements with physicians often involve helping them to understand what information patients desire. It can be boiled down to the following items:

What information does a parent or family member want to know?[8]

- How to gauge the severity of illness
- How you assess the illness
- When to seek advice
- Nature of the illness
- How the illness will affect their life
- How over-the-counter medicines and antibiotics work
- How to monitor after-discharge
- Where they can access additional information about the illness

Following is a mnemonic device for communicating with patients:[9]

- B—Background "What's going on in your life?"
- A—Affect "How do you feel about what is going on?"
- T—Trouble "What about the situation troubles you the most?"
- H—Handle "How do you handle that?"
- E—Empathy "That must have been very difficult for you."

☑ **Effective communication is the product of thoughtful strategy and effort, not chance.**

Please Mind Your Manners
By Dave Trowbridge, Service Quality Specialist

My hospitalized two-year-old son tried to be brave, but ended up crying during many tests. After two days of being poked and prodded, he asked, "Daddy, why doesn't he say please or thank you?"

I don't remember what I said, but I am sure I mentioned the doctor's very busy schedule or something along those lines. The doctor did not reply, but I could tell he was a little aggravated and somewhat embarrassed.

The doctor "remembered his manners" the following day, and it actually helped. To those little ears, "please open your mouth" sounded much better than the order "open your mouth."

---

8   J. Kai, "Parents' Difficulties and Information Needs in Coping with Acute Illness in Preschool Children: A Qualitative Study, *British Medical Journal* 313 (1996): 987-90.

9   Laurence Savett, *The Human Side of Medicine: Learning what it's like to be a patient and what it's like to be a physician* (Westport: Auburn House, 2002).

☑ **Whether young or old, people appreciate it when you mind your manners. No matter how old or young, love and compassion are universally understood.**

Notepad: "Questions for the Doctor"
By Kelly Wright, Staff Consultant

After suffering a heart attack, my grandfather was admitted to the hospital. Each evening, our entire family was there to support him. Unfortunately, doctors make their rounds during the day.

As my grandmother watched her spouse of 50 years lie in a hospital bed, hooked up to machines and enduring many tests, fear took over. What would happen? What treatments were in store? My grandma was distraught. Plus, she no longer had the best memory. Additionally, my grandpa was hard of hearing, so he didn't always catch everything the doctor said.

Each night, the family would gather and look to my grandma for answers about what the doctor or other health care professionals said earlier that day. She couldn't always remember the details. For example, a nutritionist gave instructions on the no salt/low salt diet. After the nutritionist left, my grandma wondered whether he could still eat bacon—one of the saltiest foods!

What could help this situation? A notepad or tape recorder represents one resource that would have allowed family members to write down questions and responses. Many of the best-performing hospitals that I work with make certain that one or both of these items are in all patients' rooms.

☑ **Communication between the hospital staff and the patient and family members is crucial. It allows for more knowledgeable decision making by the patient and family because they are well informed. It gives peace of mind to know that you have the correct information, and that there was no misinterpretation.**

One Physician's Bedside Manner
By Tobeter Towne, Lead Consultant

A fellow consultant moved into town and sought a pediatrician for her children. After talking with others—an illustration of "word-of-mouth" (also called "likelihood to recommend" on Press Ganey surveys)—she visited and loved a particular pediatrician. Why? The doctor not only talked to her, but also actually spoke directly to her children—and listened. It wasn't patronizing, the physician actually tuned in to the patient—the child!

I often use this story during consulting engagements when pediatrics providers ask what they can do to improve their bedside manner.

☑ **Not only did the provider's behavior impress the child, it impressed the mother. It's just another way you can WOW your patients.**

One Physician Stands Out
By Jennifer Snyder, Staff Consultant

I was recently in the hospital for a surgical procedure. This was my first time as a patient in a hospital and I was having a procedure that I did not want to have. I was very upset and very scared.

I was quickly taken to a room and a nurse came in and introduced herself. Katherine, my nurse, sat down on the bed next to me, reassuring and comforting me. After the papers were signed and the blood was drawn, she let me know that she had to attend to other patients but that I could use the call button if I needed anything. At one point during the visit, I did use the call button to contact her. Katherine quickly and cheerfully came to my bedside and got me what I needed.

Words can not describe how grateful I am to my doctor. Not only did she come in on her day off to perform the procedure, but also she took a lot of time to sit with me and my family before the surgery. All of our numerous questions were answered, and many of those questions were asked more than once. I do not have a medical degree, and, truthfully, I have no idea how competent my doctor really was. With that said, I did not have a moment's hesitation about the skill of my physician. Her kindness and compassion were reassurance enough. My sister actually said that she would drive the extra two hours just to visit this physician.

The last person that I saw before surgery was the anesthesiologist. He came into the room and immediately commanded my husband to turn off the television. (The television was on very low volume, and as apprehensive as we were about this procedure, we obviously were not listening to it.) He asked a couple of questions and he left. The only word to describe this encounter is cold.

The transporter then walked me to the operating room. On the way, we passed the anesthesiologist in the hallway. I looked him in the eye and smiled, hoping that he would give me the comfort and assurance that I so desperately needed. He just turned his head and looked away. If he had smiled, it would have been worth a thousand words to me. It would have told me that everything would be okay! Instead, he relayed to me a sense of isolation that contributed to my worries and fears.

Once inside the operating room, the transporter announced that I worked for Press Ganey. As I was lying on the table, with the anesthesiologist looking over me, he actually said, "You're the ones that make us smile." This is the last thing that I remember before the surgery and will always stay with me.

For patients, the hospital can be a very scary place. A sincere smile shows someone that you care, that you listen, and that everything will be okay!

☑ **Patients encounter dozens of care providers in their journey, but one negative encounter can shade perceptions of the entire experience.**

Astonish Your Medical Staff

Dr. Jay Kaplan, MD, FACEP, (Medical Director, Studer Group and Director of Service Excellence, California Emergency Physicians Medical Group) a frequent Press Ganey speaker and consultant, advocates the philosophy that engaging medical staff in service excellence requires first serving them with excellence.[10]

When working with your medical staff, begin by asking doctors several up-front questions: What do you want? Are you getting what you want? Do you love what you are doing? Are there things getting in the way of your loving it more?

Creating a platform of service excellence depends on your ability to engage medical staff by letting them know why service excellence is important. Dr. Kaplan suggests focusing on three platforms: reimbursement (quality hospitals attract quality physicians, quality physicians attract patients), skilled staff (you will attract more skilled staff if doctors are satisfied), and malpractice risk (lowers when patients are satisfied).

Dr. Kaplan uses the acronym CARE to explain the needs of physicians: **C—care** quality for our patients, **A—appreciation** for what we do, **R—responsiveness** to our issues, and **E—efficiency** of our practice. Building trust with your medical staff is key, but remember, it takes time. Facilitate the process by creating formal routes of communication, surveying your medical staff and asking for their input, and making physician satisfaction a regular agenda item at staff meetings.

Follow Dr. Kaplan's five physician WOWs:

- Proper use of the telephone log (when someone pages a doctor keep a log of who sent the page)
- Have information available when calling or returning calls to physicians,
- Use the patient locator log (if a patient went for lab, tests, etc., mark down where they are and when they will be back)
- Follow policy of returning charts to chart slot or order rack
- Send at least one "thank you" card every week to a physician

---

[10] J. Kaplan, "How to Astonish Your Medical Staff and Engage Physicians in Service Excellence," *The Satisfaction Monitor* (Nov/Dec 2005). Available at *http://www.pressganey.com/products_services/readings_findings/satmon/article.php?article_id=298* (Accessed November 1, 2006).

After you have engaged your physicians, ask them to do something for you. Encourage them to say thank you more often, especially to those who help them on a regular basis—nurses, hospital staff, and so on. Dr. Kaplan stated that the simplest recognition is saying "thank you" at the end of the day or shift.

> ☑ **Supporting physicians helps them become the best clinicians possible. Great service to doctors provides a platform for great service to patients.**

Checklist: Keys to Great Physician-Patient Relations
By Hugh Greeley, The Greeley Company

Inducing physicians to "buy in" to patient satisfaction requires that the hospital help physicians understand and improve their affability. This requires a large dose of persistence and simplicity. This persistence and simplicity involves keeping the importance of patient satisfaction at the forefront of physicians' minds in a simple way. Examples include the following:

- Report patient satisfaction results for each physician as a standing agenda item at all quarterly medical staff meetings
- Recognize physicians for high patient satisfaction percentiles
- Post any positive patient comments about physicians
- On a quarterly basis, publish a "Customer Service Spotlight" of top-performing physicians in the hospital newsletter or local paper
- Create and frame recognition certificates for top-performing physicians
- Periodically e-mail a Press Ganey Solution Starter tip to physicians for the questions on which they scored lower than the database average
- Ask physicians for direction: "What can we do to help you be successful with your patients at our hospital?"
- Persistence and simplicity—keep trying and keep it simple.

Chapter 4.

Cleanliness and Quiet of Physical Environment

How It's Measured

The domain "Cleanliness and Quiet of Physical Environment" is covered in two HCAHPS survey questions:

- ☑ During this hospital stay, how often were your room and bathroom kept clean?
- ☑ During this hospital stay, how often was the area around your room quiet at night?

Patients estimate the frequency of these behaviors by selecting one of four response options: Never, Sometimes, Usually, or Always.

Patients don't spend their hospital stay with a scorecard in hand, marking down the frequency of these occurrences. They rely on perception and memory recall. One extraordinarily negative or positive encounter may sway their response to one of the extremes.

The Patient's Perspective

Patients' hospital stays can be traumatic. Patients should not have to be further accosted by noise or by feeling uncomfortable because of an unclean environment.

When you walk into a bakery, what is the first thing you notice? The smell! Just as bakers don't notice the smell, the **hospital staff** becomes immune to the sights, sounds, and smells of their environment.

A recent study from the Mayo Clinic highlights the impact of noise. They measured the decibel level of sound in a Critical Care Unit and determined that it is roughly equivalent to a chainsaw or jackhammer.[11] This is a real problem that has real consequences to patient health.

To get a grip on the problem, a leader at one client facility spent the night in an empty room. The leader found that getting to sleep was going to be an uphill battle, simply because of the noise and the discomfort of the bed, pillows, and blankets. And this was without a roommate or 3:00 a.m. blood draws. After this experiment, things changed quickly. This is something that every leader who seeks to truly understand their patients' experiences should do at some point.

According to Press Ganey data, the one factor with the greatest impact on patient perceptions of quiet and cleanliness is whether the patient has a roommate. Quite simply, the score differential is so great between patients with and without roommates that it is the biggest systemic change that can be made. Think about it: when you're on vacation and in the best of spirits, you don't want to share a hotel room with a stranger. When you're sick and in the worst of spirits, it is probably the worst time to share your personal space with a stranger. To maximize patient satisfaction scores, put patients in their own rooms until you absolutely have to start using "semiprivate" rooms.

Our Stories

It Takes More Than Just "I'm Sorry"
By Barb Huffer, MA, Regional Service Manager

A sleep clinic patient, hooked up to wires and other devices, attempts to fall asleep. The TV outside his room is blasting throughout the night and the technician on monitoring duty is talking loudly on the phone.

By 4:00 a.m., he had enough of the noise. He attempted to leave the facility for at least a few hours of uninterrupted sleep at home. When he reached the locked exit door, he had to wake up the security guard to be let out!

When the first apology call came from the facility, he related exactly what happened. He got an apology for having a poor experience. By the time the

---

[11] C.A. Cmiel, D.M. Karr, D.M. Gasser, L.M. Oliphant, and A.J. Neveau, "Noise Control: A Nursing Team's Approach to Sleep Promotion," *American Journal of Nursing* 104, no. 2 (2004): 40-48. Available at *http://www.nursingcenter.com/library/JournalArticle.asp?Article_ID=483241* (Accessed: November 1, 2006).

fourth call came and the response was exactly the same as the first, he told the caller not to call again or to have anyone else from the facility call again. He let each caller know that, in his opinion, the tech behaved very unprofessionally, as did the security guard. Furthermore, his insurance company paid a lot of money for a test that did not result in any conclusive answers because he never went to sleep.

If only one of the callers had asked what could be done to make it right or offered a repeat exam at no cost, it may have turned around the patient's perception of his experience. No one made this offer. Just saying they were sorry was their limit.

Saying you're sorry is just the first step. Offering a solution or asking what the patient thinks is a fair resolution is the next. Following through with what you decide to do is imperative. Thanking the patient for bringing the matter to your attention sends the message that you truly do care and that you are learning from this encounter.

> ☑ **Following all of the steps of service recovery serves two purposes: (1) it can turn around a patient's perception of their care, which can be seen in quarterly patient satisfaction scores, and (2) it can result in the positive marketing from a now satisfied patient.**

Your Room Is as Fresh as a Daisy
By Bethany Pointer, Data Control Specialist

I've been in the hospital several times over the course of my life and, out of all of those inpatient stays, only once did I ever see someone come to clean my room. Now, this doesn't mean that my room or bathroom had not been cleaned several times throughout the course of my hospital stay, but I never really knew for sure. For me, a clean bathroom in a hospital is a big deal, especially when you are sharing a room with another patient. Without some indication or proof that someone has actually come into the room and cleaned, patients have no idea whether this work has been done.

Of the dozens of ways that cleaning staff inform a patient that their room has been cleaned, one best practice has been proven beyond all other methods. Laminated cards that read, "We've cleaned your room and now it's as fresh as a daisy." The card includes the name of the person who cleaned the room and the extension where they can be reached. To go above and beyond, leave a small vase and one fresh daisy to accompany the card.

> ☑ **Make the extra effort to let your patient know that you have cleaned their room.**

Bathroom Cleanliness
By Barb Huffer, MA, Regional Service Manager

One thing that can skew a patient's perception of wait time is the public bathroom. When the upper-respiratory flu bug hit last spring, I had to visit an urgent care center. My expectation was that the wait would be a long one and I was okay with that, but when I had to use the bathroom, my satisfaction plummeted. I won't even go into the condition of that facility, but I've used gas station facilities that were cleaner.

Since that episode, I have paid far more attention to the public bathrooms in each hospital I visit. What is the point of a beautifully appointed lobby and a well-stocked gift shop if the bathrooms have trash on the floor or the toilets need a good scrubbing?

☑ **Look at your facility from the eyes of your visitors. The smallest detail can derail a patient's perception of care.**

Who Owns First Impressions?
By Melissa Thatcher, System Consultant

I recently made a visit to Baptist Health South Florida (Coral Gables, FL). Walking into the first-floor lobby, I was greeted by a smiling uniformed security officer seated behind a desk. As I walked toward him, I noticed the desk's nameplate read "Director of First Impressions." He certainly made a good first impression on me as we chatted while I signed in and received my visitor badge.

In the elevator, I thought about how the sign signaled the hospital's awareness of how important their behavior is to forming an impression about the organization. This was a simple way of showing that their culture supports not only patient satisfaction, but understands that every interaction with patients, coworkers, families, and even visitors (like vendors and mail carriers) are worthy of their best service.

When I made my way out of the elevator, I walked up to the two ladies seated at the reception desk to introduce myself and find out where to go for my meeting. There it was again! But this time there were two nameplates bearing the title "Director of First Impressions."

This may sound simple, but these signs were powerful. Each of the "Directors" I met was empowered to take responsibility for all initial ideas and feelings I would form about Baptist Health South Florida. When you think about it, this sign tells visitors that the person behind the desk is aware that they have an opportunity to leave you with a positive or negative impression.

That's a big responsibility and one that many people don't consider. We all have the opportunity to view our daily interactions as opportunities to leave a good impression with everyone we encounter.

> ☑ **These "Director of First Impressions" signs were a reminder that, as Mister Rogers once said, "If you could only sense how important you are to the lives of those you meet; there is something of yourself that you leave at every meeting with another."**

A Good Night's Sleep: Reducing the Noise Level
By Laura Lindberg, MS, CPHQ, Knowledge Manager

Keeping the noise level down on a busy inpatient floor is a formidable challenge. With the hustle and bustle of visitors, care providers, staff, and so on continually moving through the halls, it is difficult for patients to get the rest they need. This can be especially frustrating at night. For staff on the third shift, it is difficult to remember to keep quiet because patients are sleeping.

One single idea is unlikely to reduce the noise in the facility. Facilities that are successful at improving their scores for noise level often implement a group of ideas. To begin, lights in the hallway are dimmed between 9 p.m. and 7 a.m. Although lighting may seem separate from noise levels, it sets the tone of the area as a place of rest. People are more likely to be quiet in areas that are dark and still.

Staff members turn all phone ringers to the quietest tone and all pagers to vibrate. If a call comes in over the system, the staff member answers by picking up the receiver versus shouting over a speaker phone system. This practice is conveyed to all staff members at orientation and night-shift workers are evaluated on their compliance. Overhead paging is reduced to only life and death emergencies during the nighttime hours.

As a final measure, the front desk keeps a bell. The bell is rung when the noise level gets too high. It provides an immediate reminder to quiet down. Staff members then remember to whisper and eliminate unnecessary noise from the care area.

Combining these practices helps ensure that patients have the opportunity for a good night's sleep.

> ☑ **Reducing noise level requires a series of conscientious efforts.**

Don't Be Cruel
By Lisa Daul, MBA, RD, CPHQ, Principal Consultant

Legendary nurse Florence Nightingale warned that unnecessary noise is a "major cruelty" inflicted on the sick. The military uses constant, loud sounds to wear down prisoners for more productive interrogation. Such cruelty and torture, however, are not the goals of a hospital visit. Is it time to evaluate your hospital's level of noise cruelty?

Noise causes stress for patients and health care workers. The first step is becoming aware of the noise around us. Choose appropriate locations in the hospital, and then take a moment, close your eyes to eliminate visual distractions, and listen. What do you hear? Squeaky wheels on carts, equipment alarms, multiple voices, construction, overhead pages, telephones, televisions, cellular telephone conversations, call light alarms?

Simple measures can address the cruelty of noise, including the following:

- Regularly oil the wheels on carts, gurneys, and other mobile medical equipment. Not only does it make them quieter, but also it makes them easier to move.
- Respond to equipment alarms immediately. This reduces noise levels and creates the perception that staff is available and responsive to patient needs.
- Promote a culture of "quiet." Insist that all pagers, cellular telephones, and other communication devices used by staff are set on vibrate mode.
- Eliminate all overhead pages except for hospital code situations: provide staff with handheld walkie-talkies.
- Provide private areas in which medical personnel can consult with patients and their families, or where families can be alone to discuss personal issues or make telephone calls.
- Appoint one person per shift to be the noise monitor. This person will provide gentle reminders when the verbal noise level begins to escalate.
- Take a tip from the airlines. Provide head sets for televisions or noise-canceling purposes.

Don't be cruel. Assess and address your noise issues. With the length of hospital stays being shortened, patients need to use their brief stay to focus on healing and resting. If noise prevents good rest, it can impede their healing.

☑ **Noise is stressful to patients and health care workers, but it can be reduced dramatically.**

A Splash of Color
By Julie Tabler, Lead Consultant

Hospitals are moving away from bland colors evoking sterility to using vibrant splashes of colors, such as accent walls, flowers, landscapes, and wall murals. Color adds life and zeal and pleasure. Color makes you feel good.

Pediatric facilities have known this for a long time, and inpatient adult facilities are starting to follow their lead.

Being fantastically creative does not have to cost a lot of money. Several of the best client facilities I've been to feature local artists' paintings or involve local community organizations or art students. Other facilities customized a few rooms as feminine (flowers, butterflies) and a few as masculine (golfing, racing), then match their patients with appropriate rooms.

☑ **What is pleasant to the eye is comforting to the soul.**

What a Little Color Can Do
By Beth Heck, Regional Service Manager

Everyone knows "hospital corridor" color. Hospitals are meant to be a place for healing, yet most are visually cold and sterile.

When visiting Boca Raton Community Hospital (Boca Raton, FL), my contact took me on a tour of their hospital and I noticed that something stood out. The walls in the hallways and rooms had been painted with murals of flowers, sunrises, sunset, and island settings. A local group of women artists had volunteered their time to make the hospital beautiful. One of the women in the group had been a patient in the hospital. While recovering, she realized that the visuals in the rooms were not helping her heal but making her feel trapped. She decided to do something to make a change.

The Pediatrics Unit stood out to me the most. Former child patients had been recruited to help. The paintings reflect the children and what makes them happy and this gives the children an escape from the day-to-day struggles of being hospitalized.

Giving patients something beautiful to see every day promotes their sense of a healing experience and satisfaction.

☑ **Making a small difference to patients is not difficult. Painting the walls did not cost the hospital anything, yet it improved the patient perception of the hospital environment tremendously.**

Clean Out the Junk

At Memorial Hermann Southeast Hospital (Houston, TX), their new CEO called for all posters, flyers, and excess information to be taken down from the walls. The reason? Doing so created a cleaner atmosphere for patients and family members. Announcements and informational postings are allowed in employee areas (e.g., break rooms, nursing stations, etc.), but general public areas have a clean, professional look.

The only wall décor are paintings and photographs by local artists. The frames all match and the pictures or paintings have similar themes. They have three major "sections" of the facility and the artwork helps tie these three areas together.

> ☑ **Sometimes, a clean appearance necessitates eliminating cluttered walls and halls.**

Maintenance Rounding
By Katie Drevs, System Consultant

The service excellence program at Brockton Hospital (Brockton, MA), a Press Ganey Success Story Winner, calls for a member of the maintenance department to visit every patient within 24 hours of the patient's admission. During this visit, the member runs through a checklist to ensure that all equipment is working properly, answers questions about how the equipment works, fixes anything not working properly, introduces the service hotline, and generally stays in touch with patients and their needs.

Wake Forest University Baptist Medical Center (Winston-Salem, NC) has a maintenance hotline with a mandatory turnaround time of 30 minutes for all calls. Other hospitals give the maintenance staff pagers and then give patients those pager numbers. This makes it easier for maintenance staff to hit the 30-minute deadline as they stop by the patient's room on the way to or from other locations, which is particularly important for large campuses.

> ☑ **Quickly get to patients' rooms to address spills and broken equipment. Better yet, stay one step ahead and anticipate needs by making rounds during admission.**

Show Me the Way
By Michelle M. Gloss, MS, System Consultant

Frustration with "way-finding" causes patient and visitor dissatisfaction with your hospital. Insufficient signage and the lack of other "way-finding" materials (e.g., maps) can cost your hospital thousands of dollars each year in hidden costs. Getting lost on the way to or inside the hospital causes unnecessary stress for patients and visitors.

How easy is it to find your hospital? Once inside, how easy is it to find one's way around? How do you know whether your hospital needs to improve "way-finding"? Consider the following tests:

- Be a new patient. Drive to your hospital using only the current existing signs. Did the signs take you directly to your hospital? Or, did they direct you to another hospital? Did you ever make a wrong turn? Were the signs helpful only in getting you to the campus and then you were left on your own?

      Once inside, try to get to a department by using only existing signage. Where will patients get lost? Are there signs reassuring patients that they're going in the right direction?

- Check existing patient complaints. How many complaints are about not being able to find your hospital or about making their way around the hospital? Poll the staff at your information desks, gift shops, security, and so on—anywhere patients are likely to make a first contact. How often do staff hear complaints about patients or visitors getting lost?
- Ask your patients. Are they having a difficult time finding their way around? Are they late for appointments because they couldn't find the right department or unit?
- Solicit the feedback of nonpatient visitors. Use mystery shoppers or enlist the help of your Press Ganey consultant or account executive. Did she or he have any trouble finding your hospital? How long did the trip take? How long should it have taken?

Following are recommendations from the seminal report *Designing the 21ˢᵗ Century Hospital*:[12]

- Before the visit, mail patients copies of maps and written directions
- In the hospital, use:
  - "you-are-here" maps and directories at key entries
  - directional signage at decision points
  - reassurance signs for long paths

    ☑ **Reduce stress for your patients and save time for your staff and money for your hospital by making it easy to get to and around your facility.**

Hotel Services
By Beth Heck, Regional Service Manager

Today's hospitals have a unique challenge to satisfy their patients. Today's consumers are an educated and demanding group. People have very high

---

[12]   R. Ulrich, C. Zimring, X. Quan, A. Joseph, and R. Choudhary, "The Role of the Physical Environment in the Hospital of the 21st Century: A Once-in-a-Lifetime Opportunity," Report to The Center for Health Design for the Designing the 21st Century Hospital Project (Robert Wood Johnson Foundation, 2004).

standards of customer service. When in the hospital, patients expect the facility to have the same amenities found in the hotel and airline industries.

For most, this is an unfair assumption. Even the shortest stay in a hospital requires the teamwork of many highly trained and skilled people, multiple test and procedures to be run, many different medications that may change from time to time, and the need for highly technological equipment. The challenge is to determine how to offer a safe and healing environment for the patient as well as all of the comforts and services individuals expect to find in hotels.

Here are some ways facilities succeeded in meeting this challenge:

- VIP Rooms—These rooms are available to patients for an additional fee, but they are completely private, offer more hotel-like amenities for patients (e.g., a private hall, toiletries, room service ordering with upscale dining options, decorating more like a hotel room, comfortable chairs, and additional beds for guests).
- Concierge Services—Many facilities have implemented concierge services in their lobbies. Instead of the traditional volunteers and greeters, hospitals have hired concierges from the hotel industry to assist patients and guests with their personal needs.
- Room Service Meal Ordering—This allows guests to have a choice in their meals. Give daily menus with a few options for patients based on their dietary needs with a direct phone number to place their orders.
- Private Rooms—Hospitals are making the move to offer a greater number of single rooms for patients to offer privacy and space.
- Hotel-Like Décor—A simple change for facilities includes improving the décor of the halls and rooms. Add color and artwork to give a space a more "home-like" feel.
- Spa Service—Offer fee-based spa services such as haircuts, facials, manicures, pedicures, and massages for patients. These services provide an extra comfort and give patients something to look forward to during their stay.
- Scheduling Guarantees—Airlines run within specified time frames. Offer scheduling time frames and guarantees for tests, procedures, and discharge. If you cannot meet these deadlines, offer an explanation as to why, establish when the next deadline will be, and be prepared for service recovery.

☑ **Meeting or exceeding the expectations of even the most demanding patients is within reach.**

Make Purchasing a Win-Win Situation
By Aris Relias, Senior Consultant

A top performer purchases new furniture differently. Typically, this purchasing is handled by a few individuals who are not directly affected by their selections. When it came time to purchase new office furniture, room décor, and miscellaneous furniture in their area, they gave their employees the ability to vote on what they liked. To make this happen, they not only posted detailed pictures throughout the hospital, but also took over an area restaurant for an evening and set up all of the furniture for the employees to look at, touch, and get a true sense of what they liked.

This practice had two results. First, purchases had greater effectiveness—everything fit the needs of the affected teams and areas. Second, this increased employee satisfaction, particularly with participation—a key driver of employee loyalty. This facility not only improved the hospital environment, employees felt like their opinions truly mattered.

> ☑ **Involving employees in decision making about the hospital environment results in a win-win situation for patient and employee satisfaction.**

Checklist: Noise Level In and Around Patient Rooms

Following is a checklist to help establish an acceptable noise level in and around patient rooms:

- Create a new policy on overhead paging
- Provide an e-mail address to hospital staff
- Provide ear phones for patient televisions
- Lower ringer volumes for all phones
- Create a family pager notification system in surgery
- Offer wireless phones in key areas
- Provide wireless phones for nurses
- Install carpets in hallway
- Close doors to patient rooms (obvious but true)
- Display reminder signs for staff throughout floors
- Write staff newsletter articles that address the need to lower noise levels and the associated benefits
- Repair squeaky carts
- Create awareness of noisy times (rounds, shift change, meal time)

Chapter 5.

Pain Control

How It's Measured

The domain "Pain Control" is covered in three HCAHPS survey questions:

- ☑ During this hospital stay, did you need medicine for pain? Yes or No → If No, Go to Question 15 (i.e., skip the next two questions).
- ☑ During this hospital stay, how often was your pain well controlled?
- ☑ During this hospital stay, how often did the hospital staff do everything they could to help you with your pain?

The direction to skip the next two questions is designed to limit responses only to those patients who received pain medication. Patients who did not receive pain medication might respond anyway. Patients estimate the frequency of these behaviors by selecting one of four response options: Never, Sometimes, Usually, or Always.

Notice the question asks about the frequency of *well controlled pain*. This implies that the hospitalization is not entirely pain-free. Pain will occur and it's the hospital staff's response to keeping that pain within tolerable limits which this question asks patients to evaluate. Patients will look back to recall if at any time their pain felt out-of-control or beyond their capacity for toleration. One extraordinarily negative or positive pain experience may sway their response to one of the extremes.

The Patient's Perspective

Patients' experiences of pain differ. What is extraordinarily painful to one person may be barely noticeable to another. Furthermore, patients' abilities to tolerate pain differ drastically. Next, patients' expectations regarding pain to be experienced and pain control differ. Finally, patients' expectations of hospital staffs' ability to control pain differ substantially as well. With all of these factors affecting patient ratings, it should be clear that effective pain control comes down to diligently ascertaining and meeting individual patient needs.

Clinicians and scientists don't fully understand the phenomenon of pain. Given this, we can't expect patients to fully understand it. Patients need to be educated about what they can expect regarding pain during their procedure as well as what they can expect regarding pain control before, during, and after their procedure.

Likewise, clinicians often need substantial education as well. Many misconceptions about the addictive nature of various analgesics or patients being drug seekers may color hospital staff reactions to patients' pain expressions and pain relief needs.

Our Stories

Preparing Patients Pays Off
By Katie Drevs, System Consultant

The "Arthritis Society" is a comprehensive pre-op program at one of our best-performing clients. It prepares elective surgery patients who have or are at risk for arthritis. The 90-minute classes educate the patient about the disease and the effected joint. The program provides education about what to expect during the surgery and the rehabilitation and life afterward. It uses testimonials and actual people who had the surgery doing day-to-day tasks. People who require more information beyond the classes receive individual follow up.

According to the program's administrator,

> A patient who understands what's going on is more comfortable with the entire procedure. They understand the process, the rationale, the timing of events, and so on. Patients thus become willing participants in the process rather than feeling like pawns in what may seem an overwhelming experience.

Newton Wellesley Hospital (Wellesley, PA) offers videos showing patients going through such maneuvers as getting out of a bath, following techniques that help with dressing, and walking with crutches. This helps patients realize they too will be able to do this after surgery.

☑ **Preparing patients for their inpatient experience before they arrive (e.g., what to expect, etc.) makes patients less fearful and enables you to establish expectations up front.**

Shore Health System (Easton, MD)
"Pain Management Program"
By Chris Mullikin—Manager, Pain Management/Palliative Care,
Memorial Hospital (Eaton, MD)

In 1996, Memorial Hospital in Easton, Maryland and Dorchester General Hospital in Cambridge, Maryland affiliated to form Shore Health System. Pain management efforts also merged, and the Pain Management/Palliative Care Committee was developed. The Pain Management/Palliative Care Committee is an interdisciplinary committee whose membership includes physicians, staff nurses, managers, pharmacologists and directors from a variety of departments. The Committee's purpose is "To create and maintain an efficient care delivery system that will support appropriate pain management for patients/residents of Shore Health System." A literature review indicated that increasing numbers of health care institutions are finding that pain management/palliative care programs are welcome additions to their vision of promoting quality health care. The program addresses six core strategies as noted in the Shore Health System Strategic Plan that was developed. Identification of the problem began with data collection by the Pain Management/Palliative Care Committee and included Press Ganey Patient Satisfaction results, which showed Shore Health System at a disappointing 28th percentile. This revelation resulted in developing strategies to increase patient satisfaction, including pain management, as part of employee orientation, adoption of Pain Rating as the fifth vital sign to be assessed every time vital signs are taken, revision of the Patient's Bill of Rights identifying appropriate pain management as a patient expectation and adoption of an administrative policy identifying appropriate pain management as a priority at Shore Health System. The challenge now is to maintain those improvements, strengthen and expand the existing pain management services and focus on identified weak links as Shore Health System strives to be the regional community provider of health and enhanced quality of life to the population it serves.

☑ **Pain management and palliative care committees can drive staff education and organizational change. Appointing passionate, clinically proficient, and well-respected people to the team will make it an effective agent for changing the behavior of clinical staff.**

Haven't Got Time for the Pain
By A Patient

When I was in the ED triage room with a severe infection, the triage nurse took down my symptoms, diagnosis, and level of pain (seven). Forty-five minutes later, the aide led me back to the exam room, annoyed as I trailed far behind. No assistance or wheelchair was offered. I didn't ask for one because I had no idea of the walk's distance.

After three hours, my pain level was assessed again and I was promised pain medication. After 20 minutes, I called the nurse's station to let them know no one had given me any pain medication yet. Another 15 minutes later, the CT tech arrived to take me for a scan, but I refused to go until after I received pain medication. I knew I couldn't stay still for the scan given my current level of pain. The CT tech was able to find the nurse and get me the medication.

I was in the ED for four hours with a pain level of seven before getting any type of relief, which I found completely unacceptable. My blood pressure was through the roof because of the pain and, despite being exhausted, I couldn't sleep. The long wait would have been tolerable if I had been pain-free.

In January 2001, the pain standards became a part of the formal survey and accreditation process for Joint Commission.[13] Prompt treatment of pain and proactive pain abatement are two main elements of the standards. Being pain-free is the right of the patient.

☑ **Patients depend on clinical staff to relieve pain throughout their stay. Being reactive—addressing pain only when patients demand it—isn't effective. Many patients don't know what level of pain is acceptable and are reluctant to approach nurses.**

Process Changes Improve Pain Management
By Peter Lanser, MSA, CPHQ, FACHE, Vice President of Press Ganey Physician and Employee Business Unit

Beebe Medical Center (Lewes, DE) is one facility that has improved pain management by focusing on the issue and changing processes. According to Sue Howell, registered nurse (RN), Beebe's Director of Inpatient Care,

> Control of pain afforded us many opportunities at Beebe Medical Center. As patients are well educated in their rights and disease processes, it became apparent that we could improve in pain management. To change the process of pain control we reviewed charts, analyzed our Press Ganey scores and comments regarding

[13] The Joint Commission on Accreditation of Healthcare Organizations, "Improving the Quality of Pain Management Through Measurement and Action," in *Monograph* (Oakbrook Terrace, IL: JCAHO, March 2003). Available at *http://www.ampainsoc.org/pub/bulletin/nov02/poli1.htm* (Accessed November 1, 2006).

pain, researched literature, talked with staff, and brought in an outside resource to discuss pain control with physicians and nurses. This lecture and the research were an eye opener for our medical center. An interdisciplinary team was formed to revamp the tools used for assessment and documentation and reevaluate the types of medication and methods of administration. Process changes included:

1. Ordering new PCA pumps (Patient-Controlled Analgesia)
2. Increasing the number of available PCA pumps
3. Creating a new flow sheet used by anesthesia and nursing
4. Initiating PCA pumps in PACU (Post-Anesthesia Care Unit)
5. Including only IV analgesia on the revised pain order sheet
6. Including alternative methods of pain control on the revised orders
7. Increasing PCA usage for abdominal as well as orthopedic surgery

All the inpatient units focused attention on details and patient comfort. Physicians, nurses, and nursing assistants began taking pain control seriously. The results were encouraging—these process changes resulted in an improvement from the eighty-seventh percentile to the ninety-ninth percentile in just one-quarter for the Press Ganey survey question *"How well your pain was controlled?"*

☑ **Be sure to look at all areas in your facility in order to identify ways to improve. Sometimes a successful improvement process will apply to areas you haven't thought of yet (i.e., what works for pre-surgery, may work for post-surgery and even areas outside of surgery as well). Be willing to probe deeper into the lower scoring areas to determine what makes those patients and their care different from the higher scoring patients.**

Pain Experience Begins with Expectations
By A Press Ganey Client

I have heard hundreds of "they hurt me so bad" stories followed by "it was so much better when you did it." The only difference between the patients making these statements was in how they were prepared before, communicated with during, and talked to after the procedure.

The biggest component in managing pain is communication. Patients will experience pain—there is no way around it. But it's really not the pain that is the problem. The problem begins with patients' expectations. Top performers manage expectations in the following ways:

- Tell patients ahead of time what pain to expect. Be specific. Never exaggerate or minimize expectations. Perhaps the most dreaded words are "this won't hurt," because they usually mean that it will.
- Ask patients directly about their pain.
- Reassure them that the pain they experience is normal.
- Let them know that you can't always eliminate the pain, but you can help them control it and cope with it.
- Let them know that you are there to help.

Three common instances for managing patient expectations regarding pain are pain in bed, pain during transfers, and pain during activities.

Pain in bed

A patient is in bed, hurting. They do nothing but sit and watch the clock waiting for their pain meds. To help the patient, nurse, family members, therapists, and other staff, have the nurse write on the whiteboard the date, "next PM (Pain Medicine)," and the time (adding five minutes after when they can actually get it (e.g., if they can receive their medication every four hours, write the time for four hours and five minutes). Patients then have a system for remembering when they will next receive their pain medication. The nurse then shows up either at the time written on the board or five minutes early and distributes the pain medication proactively. If the patient still has to ask when they will receive their medication, then the system did not work. The patient and everyone entering the room should know what to expect.

Pain during transfers

The patient knows that transfer is going to hurt. This is often rooted in fear and lack of control. This anxiety can be reduced through communication.

- Let patients know what you will do to reduce pain during transfer.
- Let the patient feel a sense of control by encouraging them to participate in the transfer in some way. Let the patient do some of the work. Tell the patient, "You are in charge and we will move at your pace." The person doing the transfer assists the patient in moving, asking, "What can I do to help?" and saying, "You tell me if it is hurting, I will be as gentle as possible."
- Explain exactly what you are going to do before you touch the patient. Communicate exactly what you are doing as you do it. The tendency is to rush, but you must move at the patient's pace. Make sure that everyone is trained in the proper transfer techniques along with the proper scripting when transferring a patient.

Pain during activities

By telling the patient that pain is expected and that you will do whatever you can to make things comfortable, you prepare them for the possibility of discomfort. Tell them exactly what you are going to do before you do it so that they have time to prepare. It is important to ensure that the patient has pain medication before the transfer or assure them you will get them pain medication soon after the transfer.

> ☑ **This may seem relatively basic, but managing patients' expectations, participation, and communication related to pain will affect patients' perceptions regarding their pain as much or more than their actual physical pain.**

Communication = Comfort
By A Patient

I needed to have knee surgery and was a bit scared. The last time I had surgery it was to have my tonsils removed and I was 16 years old. Back then, my mom was there to know what was going on and to make it all better. I chose to have the surgery done at the freestanding surgery center associated with my doctor's office. The center was unfamiliar and I didn't have anyone for guidance and comfort. Thus, the day of surgery came with great trepidation.

Upon arrival, I was pleasantly surprised by the communication among staff. Every person who walked into my treatment area started off by repeating what the last person said or did, and then informed me what would happen next. This happened with four different people. They all sounded scripted because they all even used the same words and phrases. The knowledge of what was going to happen and the teamwork evidenced by the scripted communication reduced my fears.

I am on an insulin pump and required a little different preparation and care from the average patient because of my pump. It was also comforting to hear a new person come in and state that they knew I was on an insulin pump and what had been done to it so far. The nurse in the recovery room was even familiar with what I was supposed to do with the pump once I woke up.

I had complete comfort with the staff in every way, all because they all seemed to know my case personally! A little communication outside of the patient's room leads to large amounts of comfort for the patient.

> ☑ **You might know everything about the patient's treatment and care, but the patient won't know you know unless you tell them.**

Educate Staff on Effective Pain Management
Peter Lanser, MSA, CPHQ, FACHE, Vice President of Press Ganey
Physician and Employee Business Unit

Duncan Regional Hospital (Duncan, OK) is extremely proud of the work being done by its staff to educate the staff, patients, and family members on pain control. A great deal of work, planning, and "creative" education has been put into place with an emphasis on ensuring that Duncan's patients do not suffer from pain.

Gina Flesher, RN, Education Instructor, and Cindy Rauh, RN, Director of Acute Care Services, state that,

> Pain is the number one symptom of the majority of all patients we see at DRH. It is the goal of the staff to ask 100 percent of our patients on admission to the ED if they are in pain. If the answer is a "yes," the next goal is to treat that pain within 30 minutes and reassess the intervention to bring that pain down below the level of 5 (on a scale of 1-10) within two hours. We are aggressive in our pain management, recognizing that the patient's self-report of pain is considered the single most important indicator of pain.

The hospital's monthly newsletter "Viewbox" includes a monthly column to educate not only the nursing staff, but also the entire staff, on the hospital's commitment to making sure our patients are comfortable.

> ☑ **Pain is an important component of patient care. Proper diligence should be given to see that pain is a recognized area of focus for all improvement efforts.**

How One Hospital Went from Laggard to Leader in Pain Management
By Paul Alexander Clark, MPA, MA, FACHE, Director of Knowledge Management

The Nursing Department at Brattleboro Memorial (Brattleboro, VT) has focused on pain management for more than eight years—years before the Joint Commission on Accreditation of Healthcare Organizations (JCAHO) initiated pain management as the "Fifth Vital Sign." A standing Pain Committee has been meeting regularly since 1995 and spearheads improvements in quality, service, and education.

Despite being a small rural hospital, Brattleboro has devoted significant resources to organizational learning and development of knowledge and skills among the nursing staff. Many learning materials and texts were obtained through monetary donations to the hospital to improve care in specific areas (e.g., pain, diabetes, etc.). Nurses and nurse managers have presented their knowledge, experiences, and improvement initiatives at various conferences and conventions. These ongoing learning efforts help the organization continuously improve in tandem with or ahead of advancements in health care at large. Wendy Cornwell, RN, as Director of Education, coordinates these learning activities and co-leads many customer service initiatives. Pain assessment, patient education, and the support of senior leadership have been integral to success.

Best practices implemented by Brattleboro Memorial include the following:

- *Pain Assessment and Frequent Reassessment*—Nurses must perform a formal pain assessment each day, filling out an assessment form that includes the patient's own qualitative description of the nature of whatever pain they have experienced. Patients are asked to rate their current level of pain and to estimate an acceptable level of pain. The pain relief strategy is also documented—whether it be analgesics, repositioning, pillows, or other nonpharmacological methods. Nurses must reassess patients at regular intervals throughout the day; there is a column on the nursing flowchart to fill in the patient's pain rating at that particular time. The medical history chart has space designated for the patient's pain rating history (e.g., ratings experienced, maximum tolerance, preferred pain relief methods, etc.).

  The ultimate goal is to reassess patients and provide pain relief before they begin to feel discomfort or pain. As a standard, technicians frequently ask each patient to explain how they are feeling and to rate their pain during any tests or procedures. Radiology performs a formal pain assessment when patients receive their services; this assessment is also included in the patient's chart.

  Everyone in the hospital is capable of assessing patients' pain, soliciting a pain rating from the patient, and providing either pain relief or a swift referral.

- *Preoperative Assessment*—Elective surgery patients come in for a preoperative assessment appointment in their physician's office, which includes a pain assessment. The patient is given the *contact information for the anesthesiologist* in case they have any questions or wishes to discuss anesthesia options before surgery.

- *Actively Elicit and Meet Patients' Pain Control Preferences*—For elective surgery, patients are asked during preadmission for their pain management preferences and whether they want to receive information on pain management. Preferences are also elicited following the procedure in the assessment because preferences may change during the experience of hospitalization, surgery, or pain. Patient preferences and beliefs are respected and met to the best of the hospital's ability. This includes providing the opportunity for numerous *alternative and complementary therapies*. Patients have access to numerous complementary pain treatments, including reiki, acupuncture, acupressure, facials, music therapy, hypnotherapy, pet therapy, and so on. These options are most frequently used by oncology patients (or other patients managing a chronic illness). Adjustments are readily made for patients' beliefs and preferences. For example, a medicine man was brought in at the request of a Native American patient. Oncology patients regularly integrate a spiritual focus into their pain treatment regimen—patients may use prayer to cope with pain and nurses will pray with patients if they are asked to do so. The Education and Nursing Departments regularly collaborate with *Sojourns*, a local community health clinic specializing in complementary and alternative therapies.

- *Organizationwide Training*—Everyone in the organization (housekeeping, receptionists, admitting clerks, administrators, etc.) participated in two training seminars. The first was on customer service and the standards of behavior (see below for more information). The second was on pain management: what to do if you encounter a patient or guest in pain, how to quickly triage pain, and how to help the patient or guest. This enabled everyone in the organization to recognize patients in pain and do something about it—even if it was just to ask patients if they felt all right and whether they could use some help. For example, if a housekeeping staff member sees that a patient is in pain, she or he goes to get the nurse. Or if an admitting clerk sees that a guest is making pained expressions, she or he inquires and makes an appropriate referral. Every employee has learned how to assess pain.

- *Mandatory, Ongoing Pain Management Education/Training for Nurses*— Pain management training is required above and beyond continuing education standards. For example, every nurse must earn continuing education credits in transitioning patients from IV to oral analgesics. Education must be an ongoing process because a major, ever-present obstacle is getting clinicians to accept that whatever the patient says about their pain is reality. Patient comments from the surveys related to pain are highlighted or reviewed in all training sessions. Nurses receive advanced training in the important "soft" skills of compassion, understanding, empathy, kindness, courtesy, and focusing on the patient.

- *Comprehensive Pain Information and Education Resources*—Numerous educational and informational resources on pain management are available for nurses and clinicians to consult. Many of these have been purchased through the support of donations, including the following:

- *JCAHO videos*—Explain JCAHO pain management standards and demonstrate them in practice.
- *Pain: A Clinical Manual*—A comprehensive book by Margo MaCafferey and Chris Pasero is frequently consulted by nurses. The spiral binding makes it easy to make photocopies for patient education. At least one copy is in every nursing unit.
- *Pain Education (Aspen)*—Another book full of easily reproducible pages for patient education purposes. These resources also help to remind and reeducate staff on the pathophysiology of pain control.
- *Pain Resource Manual*—The Pain Committee compiled a catalog of local resources available help patients cope with pain, including massage therapists, psychiatric therapy, pain clinics, complementary therapies, etc. The information is especially useful for patients experiencing chronic pain.
- *Pain Notebook*—An organizational learning tool wherein various people within the hospital proactively contribute sections dealing with pain in their area of expertise. The resource is a living document, continuously updated and tailored to the hospital, with sections on acute pain, cancer pain, pediatric pain, and other types of pain. It includes the contact information for the people who make entries in the notebook to serve as further consultants if needed.

- *Pain Clinic*—Ongoing 15-minute sessions held within medical staff meetings and specifically designed to educate medical staff (physicians). Education and training are provided on charting and documentation to meet nurses' requirements for patients' pain control. The clinics describe how to rate and assess pain, the inherently subjective nature of pain (i.e., "pain is what the patient says it is"), and nonpharmacological routes for pain relief. The clinics keep physicians updated on new developments and techniques for pain management. Because medical staff has a limited amount of time, these clinics are kept succinct. This was the most difficult quality improvement component to implement—sometimes physicians did not take the issue of pain seriously. Physicians often failed to recognize the value in rating pain; they could not see a difference between a pain rating of 6 and 1.
- *Pharmacology Updates*—The pharmacy director attends all physician medical staff meetings. At each meeting, a 15-minute briefing is delivered educating physicians on pharmacology issues, including the following:

  - Topical Analgesics—When and how to use heating pads, lidocaine patches, and so on
  - Tylenol®—When is it too much?

- *Pain Rounds with Medical Staff*—Medical staff gather and work together on more complex cases in managing and relieving patients' pain.
- *Support Physicians' Needs in Patient Pain Management*—There are many ways that a hospital can support and assist medical staff in their role to meet patients' pain management needs. This hospital held luncheons to solicit physicians' needs in dealing with patients with chronic pain as well as repeat patients who may seek to abuse the system. Physicians responded positively to the hospital's offer to help and readily provided feedback and suggestions (which were, for the most part, wholly adopted).
- *Post-op Standing Orders*—The Pain Committee worked with physicians to develop a few post-op standing orders to avoid a situation in which the patient desperately needs pain relief immediately following surgery, but the physician is unavailable to write a prescription. For example, patient-controlled analgesia (PCA) pumps are available automatically for anyone on continuous oximetry.
- *Post-op Pain Survey*—In addition to pain assessments, patients receive a paper and pencil survey asking them to describe and rate their postoperative pain. Used for individual patients and for quality improvement purposes (to detect patterns of care or problems in or with specific procedures). The survey specifically asks about a patient's pain immediately following the procedure.
- *Unit Staffing Levels*—The ratio of nurses, nurse aides, or other staff to patients may vary by unit; one or more units may be severely understaffed. Understaffing leads to delays in responses to patients in pain as more demands infringe on assessing pain, delivering pain relief, and ensuring continuous reassessment and relief. This hospital did not find out that their Post Anesthesia Care Unit (PACU) was egregiously understaffed and overworked until interviewing a patient who had written a letter about an exceptionally poor experience in the PACU.
- *Pain Education upon Admission*—Patients are educated on pain, pain assessment, and pain management. An education and information sheet entitled "About Your Pain" is included in the admissions packet. It establishes expectations about what kind of pain they might experience, explains how pain can affect their daily life and function, and states that they have a right to have their pain treated. The exercise of that right is encouraged through the provision of detailed examples of pain rating scales. A special version of this information and education sheet was created for pediatrics. Finally, an information sheet on pain medication and taking other medications is included. Admissions clerks remind patients to review this information.

- *Ensure Pain Relief in Postdischarge*—This hospital's approach to pain management is framed by the continuum-of-quality-care philosophy, which envisions a postdischarge experience that is as pain-free as possible. If patients are being discharged to their homes, nurses ensure that they are discharged with appropriate pain medication. For patients discharged to nursing home or assisted living facilities, the Pain Committee regularly reviews cases to ensure that these patients continue to receive the appropriate level of analgesics in the nonacute setting. These reviews identified several physicians who were routinely derelict in continuing the prescription for the new facility. These physicians were counseled and coached and the problem was resolved. Still, the monitoring and review continues.
- *Standing Pain Committee*—This committee was organized several years before the Joint Commission made pain the "Fifth Vital Sign" and has been responsible for the vast majority of quality improvements related to pain management (and patient satisfaction with pain control). A highly diverse group makes up the committee with representatives from nursing, medical staff, radiology, oncology, service excellence, and the hospital ethics committee. The committee was empowered to execute whatever changes they saw fit—they kept senior leadership informed but had full authority to see change through.
- *Visible Senior Leadership Support*—Pain control and service excellence are both part of the hospital's annual and long-term strategic plans. The Pain Committee has frequently created educational presentations for the hospital board (including sending the board educational materials on pain). Whenever the committee chairs run out of ideas or need direction, they go to the Quality Council and seek their guidance (who readily provide ideas and suggestions). Monetary support has never been withheld from leadership for past initiatives.

> ☑ **Making a significant move from worst to first requires multiple, intensive interventions and many years of persistent practice. Don't get discouraged, but also don't delude yourself by searching for one magic bullet.**

Checklist: Proven Pain Management Practices

The following is a checklist of proven tactics to improve patients' pain management experience. For more details on any item, refer to the previous stories.

- Check the frequency of pain assessments and reassessments. These may need increased.

- Conduct a formal preoperative assessment *with the patient and family.*
- Use effective communication tactics:
  - ☑ Early and often, educate patients and family what pain to expect.
  - ☑ Explain to patients what you will do before doing it.
  - ☑ Tell patients and family what you are doing to reduce their pain.
  - ☑ Ask patients or family for their assistance during their care.
  - ☑ Ask patients for their pain control preferences. Do whatever possible to accommodate.

- Educate your staff on pain management:
  - ☑ Create a pain committee
  - ☑ Establish standards and guidelines for recognizing and treating pain.
  - ☑ Resolve any misconceptions regarding the addictive properties of analgesics.
  - ☑ Devote a section of your newsletter or Intranet to pain. Consider a newsletter devoted solely to pain management.
  - ☑ Obtain educational resources for staff reference. Place directly on the unit to promote use.
  - ☑ Devote 15 minutes in every medical staff meeting to educate the physicians on pain management and their role in ensuring successful patient experiences.

- Involve pharmacists in staff education, patient education, and improvement initiatives.
- PCA may be underutilized. Track usage and compare across units or system. Increase as needed.
- Evaluate your staffing levels. Nurse-to-patient ratios influence the effectiveness of pain management.
- Include nonanalgesic and complementary therapies in your pain management protocols.
- Be proactive and include pain questions in multiple daily rounds.
- Include the ED in your improvement efforts. For patients admitted through the ED, their pain experience in the ED waiting or treatment area will likely affect their evaluations.
- Use the whiteboards in patients' rooms to write their pain goal. Include a magnet of the pain scale on the board as both a teaching tool for the nurse and a reminder for the patient and family.
- Have all nurses on appropriate units sign a commitment to give pain medications around the clock as ordered for the first 24 to 48 hours post-operation. This signifies the importance the organization places on pain management and increases the level of commitment among nurses.

Chapter 6.

Discharge Information

How It's Measured

The domain "Discharge Information" is covered in three HCAHPS survey questions:

☑ After you left the hospital, did you go directly to your own home, to someone else's home, or to another health facility? Own home, Someone else's home, or Another health facility
→ If Another, Go to Question 21 (i.e., skip the next two questions).

☑ During this hospital stay, did doctors, nurses, or other hospital staff talk with you about whether you would have the help you needed when you left the hospital?
→ Yes or No

☑ During this hospital stay, did you get information in writing about what symptoms or health problems to look out for after you left the hospital?
→ Yes or No

The instructions to skip the next two questions at the beginning is designed to exclude patients who were discharged to another health facility (e.g., nursing home, assisted living, etc.). Patients who were discharged to their own homes or someone else's home might respond anyway.

The Patient's Perspective

The discharge process questions focus on two things: (1) coordination of care among the care team and an external health facility, and (2) written discharge information about future symptoms or health problems.

For the former, "talk with you about whether you would have the help you needed" could be interpreted broadly by patients to apply to any number of health care services, products, and issues related to their care immediately following hospitalization, such as the following:

- Medication acquisition and management
- Medical equipment acquisition, learning, practice, and use
- Rehabilitation activities (e.g., physical therapy, occupational therapy)
- Follow-up appointments for additional tests and therapies, or with primary care and specialty physicians
- Adjusting or converting the home to enable daily living activities
- Changing habits to accommodate new health realities

Despite the question's breadth of scope, the "Yes or No" nature of the response means that the important thing is not necessarily to address patients' every possible information need, but rather to provide them with **memorable printed information about who to contact if these questions arise.** Providing printed information increases the likelihood of recall when the patient receives the survey. Ideally, the information will be included in the discharge packet patients take home with them.

The same tactic can be used for written discharge information about future symptoms and health problems. The charge is to make certain that patients receive this information for every medication they are prescribed. Standardizing checks in multiple processes serve not only as checks but also as reminders for patients that they received the information. This means not merely giving patients the information when they receive the medication but having the charge nurse check the discharge folder to ensure that this information was included (and telling the patient and family this) or asking whether the patient received this information during postdischarge phone calls.

Don't be afraid to use bright colors or other styles of printing and presentation that make this information memorable. Remember, the key to these questions is to make certain that the patient not only receives the information but also **remembers** that they received it!

Our Stories

Cost of Delayed Discharge
By Katie Drevs, System Consultant

Research done at Vanderbilt University Medical Center (Nashville, TN) examined the importance of the discharge process in financial terms.[14] The authors concluded that a one-point gain or a one-point loss in satisfaction with the discharge process resulted in a $4,980 annual loss or gain per patient bed. Vanderbilt has 658 licensed beds. To calculate the per-patient figure, we divided the number of beds at Vanderbilt with their approximate number of admissions. With approximately 33,000 admissions, this results in additional earnings of $99 per patient if they raised their score by one point. You can gain a rough estimate of the potential financial returns for your own improvement initiative by multiplying the number of patients discharged at your facility by $99 or multiplying the number of patient beds by $4,980.

> ☑ **Dedicating resources to improving the discharge process can bring about a positive return on investment via patient loyalty.**

Rx Delivered
By Martin Wright, Solutions Consultant

Community Medical Center (Toms River, NJ) has a prescription home-delivery service. The staff coordinates with local pharmacies to fill prescriptions and have them delivered to the patient when they arrive home from the hospital. Case managers and nurses identify patients in need of assistance and work with the pharmacies to schedule their deliveries. The program improved patients' satisfaction with the discharge process and coordination of care, and decreased the average lengths of stay.

> ☑ **Look at your dissatisfactions or barriers to expeditious discharge. These may often be similar. Tackling these issues can bring serious win-win results.**

Getting Patients Out the Door
By Katie Drevs, System Consultant

South Shore Hospital (South Weymouth, MA) had problems with their discharge scores because of long waits after patients were told they would be

---

14   E.C. Nelson, R.T. Rust, A. Zahorik, R.L. Rose, P. Batalden, and B.A. Siemanski, "Do Patient Perceptions of Quality Relate to Hospital Financial Performance?" *Journal of Health Care Mark* 12, no. 4 (1992): 6-13.

discharged and long waits for escorts during peak times. The hospital staff came up with a few ideas:

- Healthy patients can leave with a responsible adult instead of waiting for an escort. The nurse is responsible for making a judgment call. The plan was first approved by the risk manager. This depends on your state or insurance company regulations.
- Volunteers were coordinated to supplement the transport staff during peak hours.
- A single escort or volunteer waits with several patients in the lobby.
- Reserved parking was provided for friends and family members picking up patients.
- Two-way radios are used by transport staff to improve communication.
- Evening discharge was instituted for working families.

> ☑ **A host of tactics can improve the flow of patients exiting the hospital. Brainstorming with your own nurses and transport staff will likely spawn numerous additional ideas.**

Compass Award Winner: Masonic Healthcare Center (Wallingford, CT)

At Masonic Healthcare Center, a multilevel health care organization, the major successful strategy was the decision to merge, and thereby solidify the integration of the performance improvement and service excellence processes. From 1999, the first year that the survey process was implemented, we have used the quality improvement concepts to address the Press Ganey findings.

The major strategies included:

- Immediate Communication of Negative and Positive Comments
- Direct Communication with the Patients
- Survey Binders
- Quality Improvement Team Meetings

Based on the above strategies, the hospital unit's action plans were developed. One of them dealt with discharge:

> **Social Services** developed a discharge packet to facilitate organization of the discharge plan. It helped clarify for patient/families the post-hospital services. The biweekly interdisciplinary team meeting improved the team's ability to anticipate dates for discharge.

Discharge planning is started on admission. Families are informed earlier about discharge plans. Family meetings for complicated discharges are part of the process.

☑   **Be sure to include all aspects of communication in your improvement strategies and put special focus on the communication that is done during your discharge process. Many times the communication, or lack of, is what sets the stage for the patient's satisfaction with the discharge process.**

Discharge Suites
By Martin Wright, Solutions Consultant

Discharge suites are a recent trend to improve patient flow and satisfaction with the discharge process. Many hospitals struggle with getting patients out of beds to get new patients in. Discharge suites are seen by many hospitals as the answer. A room separate from patient rooms, allows patients who choose to "step down" to leave their room, go to the discharge suite, and open up their bed for a new patient. This happens when a patient is recovered but has not yet been cleared for discharge by the physician. At some facilities, patients who use the discharge suite are offered compensation, such as waiving all phone charges and TV charges for that patient's stay. Discharge suites are typically well-appointed to please and entertain patients. The ultimate result in freeing up beds is improved patient flow and shorter lengths of stay for both ED and inpatient care.

UPMC Shadyside (Pittsburgh, PA) has used this tactic most successfully. Here's what Deb Kaczynski had to say about their program:

> In an effort to improve our patient throughput by "decompressing" the ED and the PACU, we have developed a "Discharge Hospitality Suite." Many discharged patients are unable to leave the hospital until later in the day due to ride availability and placement issues. This situation ties up the bed needed by an ED or surgical patient coming from the PACU. Our six-bed "Discharge Hospitality Suite" is staffed by an RN and a Nursing Assistant and provides the same level of care the patient would have received on the nursing inpatient unit. Patients must have a written discharge, received their written discharge instructions, and met clinical outcomes for discharge prior to transfer to the Hospitality Suite. While each room has a hospital bed, the unit is also furnished with some specifically "homey" types of furniture. A patient lounge includes a TV, VCR,

current movies, games, puzzles, etc. A small kitchenette with a stocked refrigerator and microwave allows a patient to snack, but meals continue to be delivered to the patient. All ancillary treatments continue (e.g., respiratory, physical therapy, nutrition counseling, etc.). If a patient agrees to transfer to the Hospitality Suite, all telephone and television charges for their entire stay are waived. Six beds may not seem like a lot, but opening six inpatient beds during midmorning has a tremendous effect on patient throughput.

☑ **If you're having problems with patient flow, examine the possibility of implementing a discharge suite.**

Patient Flow
By Renee Doren, MBA, System Consultant

East Alabama Medical Center (Opelika, AL) reduced the time it takes to transfer patients.[15] The staff at East Alabama Medical Center realized that for those patients who pass through multiple departments during their visit (emergency room to X-ray, X-ray to surgery, post-op to a room, etc.) there is a greater possibility for delays. If they streamlined the patient's journey, they could improve their patient flow process. They knew that improvement was possible. When they focused on reducing bottlenecks, they were able to lower the average transfer time from the PACU to an inpatient bed by 80 percent.

They followed a lot of PDCA cycles (Plan-Do-Check-Act), but they stated that one of the things that really made a difference for them was faxing reports to the receiving nurse's floor. Nurses weren't always able to be on the phone to take reports on patients, so there were delays until the nurses could call people back. Faxing the reports proved to be a significant culture change for the hospital, but it was much more efficient.

Because of the success this particular area had seen, the hospital started working on faxing reports from the Emergency Room to the receiving units.

☑ **Focus on tactics to reduce patient transfer time, streamline processes, and promote teamwork.**

---

[15] "Improving Patient Flow from the Post-anesthesia Care Unit to Inpatient Bed: East Alabama Medical Center," (Boston, MA: IHI, January 25, 2005). Available at *http://www.ihi.org/IHI/Topics/Flow/PatientFlow/ImprovementStories/ImprovingPat ientFlowfromthePostAnesthesiaCareUnittoInpatientBed.htm* (Accessed November 1, 2006).

Make It Memorable!

Excerpt from *Patient Satisfaction and the Discharge Process: Evidence-based Best Practices*[16]

No one remembers everything. Patients will only give you the highest rating on discharge instruction if they *remember* the instructions given. In current practice, patients and family are given important information by physicians, nurses, or discharge planners, but unless patients specifically ask, this information will not be repeated. Healthcare professionals may perceive such repetition as excessive, but patients and families find this reassuring, comforting, and more comprehensible. Examples of how hospitals are going beyond the minimum standards to make discharge instructions memorable include the following:

- Deliver information orally and hand the patient the same information in a pamphlet, brochure, etc. Return later and repeat the information explicitly applying it to the patient, using his or her name and other personal identifiers.
- Case managers can read the medical record to find out what nurses, physicians, and patient educators have told the patients. They can then reinforce any education and instructions the patient has received.
- On the day of discharge, the physician writes the patient's discharge order and speaks with the patient. Nurses and the case manager are nearby and listen to what the physician instructs the patient (and reads the physician's instructions on a standardized sheet). After the physician leaves, the nurse or case manager immediately repeats the instructions in both oral and written form.
- Use special colored paper or thicker stock for discharge instructions so that it stands out from all the other paperwork.
- Videos and audiotapes about illnesses, recovery, and self-care
- Support groups, discussions, or preadmission education sessions lead by former or current patients with a particular illness
- Bedside computers that can access the Internet and provide a virtual library, interactive simulations, and guides to online resources about the patient's illness
- Tailor all instructions to a sixth or eighth grade reading and comprehension level. Patients will only remember what they understand.

---

[16] Clark, Paul Alexander. *Patient Satisfaction and the Discharge Process: Evidence-based Best Practices.* HCPro, Inc. and Press Ganey Associates; 2006. Available from: *http://www.hcmarketplace.com*

Patient educators at East Alabama Medical Center in Opelika, AL, strictly adhere to a demonstration of comprehension standard on anything they teach the patient. This demonstration varies by subject, but most frequently, patients are asked to "show me." And prior to admission, patients may receive materials that will be needed postdischarge (e.g., sponges to prepare the skin, barometers to prepare lungs) for practice purposes.

At Greenwich Hospital (Greenwich, CT) an interactive television system provides patients with access to the Internet, e-mail, patient education, premium movies, and television at the bedside. This system also interfaces with a clinical information system and patient education videos. Nurses anywhere in the hospital can order an education video for a patient. And because the videos are digital, the nurse can create customized educational videos composed of clips tailored to the specific needs and education level of the patient. This is all generated from the nurse's computer and assigned delivery to the patient's room. At the end of each educational clip or video, short questions are asked to test comprehension. The answers are documented electronically. If the patient does not receive a passing score (80% correct), the nurse receives a fax notifying him of her that the patient did not pass and which questions were answered incorrectly. The nurse can then provide one-on-one teaching.

Greenwich faced challenges in implementing customized multimedia services. The patient education committee spent a substantial amount of time ensuring accuracy. The chief of each medical section reviewed each video appropriate to his or her expertise. Matching videos with the most common diagnosis-related groups for the hospital sometimes required considerable effort. The facility's television system network had to be replaced. Educating the nursing staff to encourage adoption and use took substantial time and effort before it became a component of daily practice. Despite all of this, Greenwich Hospital feels it was worth the trouble. The hospital is a Press Ganey Summit Award Winner by consistently achieving exceptionally high performance in patient satisfaction over many years.

> ☑ **Making your instructions memorable not only increases the likelihood that patients will recall them when responding to the HCAHPS survey but also makes it more likely that patients will actually follow the instructions when caring for themselves at home.**

Checklist: Proven Discharge Process Practices
By Katie Drevs, System Consultant

Following are a variety of proven discharge processes that are practiced at several successful health care facilities:

- *Discharge Checklist*—Many hospitals use discharge checklists to ensure completion of all activities. For example, staff at Dartmouth-Hitchcock

(Concord, NH) has a checklist for all information and educational activities.

- *Discharge Folders*—A prominently labeled folder is given to the patient who fills it with all of the information from nurses and staff throughout their stay. Before the patient is discharged, a nurse makes certain that the folder is complete and reviews the materials with the patient and family. This allows patients and families to organize their educational materials in their preferred way.
- *Discharge Video*—Banner Thunderbird (Phoenix, AZ) has a discharge video entitled "Leaving the Hospital." The video was created by a group of employees, many of whom acted in the video. It plays on the patient education channel 24 hours a day and includes topics like transportation home, care instructions, medications, and after discharge rehabilitation.
- *Thank You Cards*—A thank you card or letter sent immediately after discharge tells the patient that the organization is thinking of them postdischarge. Sometimes the card has the administrator's signature, and sometimes it is from the discharge nursing floor.
- *Follow-up Calls for Discharged Patients*—Follow-up telephone calls after discharge allow the patients to ask questions that they may not have had in the hospital. Things that may have made sense during hospitalization may be more confusing in the home environment with the patient and family members now doing all of the patient care. Discharge follow-up calls allow the patient to ask questions and to express additional thoughts—good or bad—about their experiences in the hospital. Many hospitals use this practice, well proven to significantly improve overall patient satisfaction, as well as discharge perceptions. For example:

  o Deaconess Hospital (Evansville, IN) has their call center call every patient postdischarge. If there are clinical or medical issues, a follow-up call is made by a nurse manager.

  o At Thomas Hospital (Fairhope, AL), every patient receives a postdischarge phone call. High-risk or vulnerable patients may receive several follow-up calls. Follow-up home visits are conducted by a case manager or education nurse for approximately 10-15 percent of all discharges.

- *Communication at Discharge*—It is during discharge that any lack of teamwork or coordination of care becomes most evident. This may be the worst time for the patient—they are told they are going home and they're ready, but they aren't informed of how the process works. Failure to communicate among any of the key players will likely result in a less-than-satisfactory experience for the patient. This is the last major event they experience during the hospitalization. So, whatever happens here will influence their overall perception of the experience.

Chapter 7.

Communication about Medicines

How It's Measured

The domain "Communication about Medicines" is covered in three HCAHPS survey questions:

- ☑ During this hospital stay, were you given any medicine that you had not taken before? Yes or No → If No, Go to Question 18 (i.e., skip the next two questions).
- ☑ Before giving you any new medicine, how often did hospital staff tell you what the medicine was for?
- ☑ Before giving you any new medicine, how often did hospital staff describe possible side effects in a way you could understand?

These questions assess patients' experience with receiving information about new medications, specifically the medication's purpose and potential side effects. The instruction to skip the next two questions is designed to limit responses only to those patients who received new medications. Patients who did not receive new medications might respond anyway. Patients estimate the frequency of these behaviors by selecting one of four response options: Never, Sometimes, Usually, or Always.

As mentioned previously, patients aren't keeping score throughout their stay. Their responses depend on perception and memory recall. Not only must the information be given, but also patients must remember it up to several weeks later that you gave this information.

The Patient's Perspective

Patients increasingly are wary of medication processes and the potential for medication errors in hospitals. Preventable medication errors have risen to account for 1 out of 131 outpatient deaths and 1 out of 854 inpatient deaths.[17] Inpatient deaths due to medication errors are estimated to have increased nearly 2.5 times from the 1980s to the 1990s.[18] The situation could be much worse as many near-misses are caught. Several hospital studies report a rate of 3-4 errors per 1,000 medication orders and nearly 2/3 of those were deemed "significant."[19] With increased publicity and media attention devoted to health care and medical errors, patients have become increasingly concerned with their safety during hospitalizations, abandoning a long-held assumption of safety. The relatively commonplace occurrence of errors in medication-related processes would disturb anyone who still believes in a fail-safe healthcare system.

The questions on this survey offer an opportunity for hospitals to involve patients at another level. Putting patients and staff on the lookout for errors from the first point of admission serves as a leverage point for error reduction and patient participation in their care. It's our job to make sure that patients and family are aware of the important role they play in partnering to ensure their own safe and successful recuperation.

Our Stories

Educate All Patients Up Front

Brattleboro Memorial Hospital (Brattleboro, VT) sends every patient a brochure before admission entitled "Taking Medications Safely In The Hospital." The educational material advises the patient to do the following:

17 Institute of Medicine. *To Err is Human: Building a Safer Health System.* Washington, D.C.: National Academies Press, 2000.
18 Phillips D, Christenfeld N, Glynn L. Increase in US medication error deaths between 1983 and 1993. *Lancet* 1998;351:1655.
19 Lesar TS, Briceland L, Delcoure K, Parmalee JC, Masta-Gornic V, Pohl H. Medication prescribing errors in teaching hospitals. *JAMA* 1990; 2263:2329-2334. Lesar TS, Briceland L, Stein DS. Factors related to errors in medication prescribing. *JAMA* 1997;277(4):312-317.

- Bring a list of everything you take at home—prescription medicines, over-the-counter medicines, vitamins, and herbals.
- When you first talk with the doctor or nurse, show them your list of what you take, and tell them your allergies.
- Tell your doctor you want to know the names of your medications and the reasons you will be taking them. Share your concerns.
- Look at and ask about medicines you are given, especially if they are new to you.
- Make sure the nurse checks your hospital ID band before you take any medication.
- Ask to speak with a hospital pharmacist any time during your stay if you would like to know more about your medication or if you have any concerns.
- When you are ready to go home, make sure the nurse, doctor, or pharmacist goes over each medication with you and anyone who will be of help in the future.
- Ask your nurse or doctor to help you in updating you list of medicines.

> ☑ **It's much easier to learn when relatively healthy and comfortable instead of learning while recuperating immediately after surgery. Educating elective surgery patients before admission is one great tactic for increasing awareness of medication safety.**

Involving Pharmacists in Patient Education
By Jodie Cunningham, Solutions Consultant

Pharmacist-patient communication can increase patient medication knowledge and therapy compliance. This story details a system at UPMC-Presbyterian (Pittsburgh, PA) to identify high-risk patients in need of more intensive medication education.

One goal was to provide ongoing education throughout the stay instead of providing all of the information at discharge. All patients were given a folder containing printed patient education sheets for each medication. The nurse updated the folder every time a new medication was added. The nurse also used the sheets to educate the patient every time a medication was administered. Finally, the nurses were provided algorithms to test the knowledge of patients with a specific diagnosis or medications.

· Patients on a complex medication regimen, admitted because of a drug-related problem (e.g., adverse drug reaction), or requiring additional instruction were seen by a pharmacist. They would design medication calendars, reinforce important medication information, and follow up with the patient as needed. An average of 40 minutes was spent with each patient. Many patients visited by a pharmacist had the number of administrations or medications reduced.[20]

☑ **Pharmacists can assist with the education of high-risk patients and provide assistance when planning programs.**

More Face Time with Pharmacists
By Melissa Thatcher, System Consultant

All patients can benefit from interaction with pharmacists—not simply the high-risk patients. According to the American Society of Health System Pharmacists (ASHP), patients want more face time with pharmacists.[21] Their study showed that 90 percent of patients would like to speak with a pharmacist about their medication when in the hospital. In the same study, only 23 percent recalled speaking to a pharmacist during their hospital stay.

Even if your organization is challenged by pharmacist staffing, one of your pharmacists may be willing to champion a program to make pharmacists a part of the clinical team.

Pharmacists can offer great benefits. Not only can they more authoritatively answer patients' questions regarding medications, but also they can help control costs and reduce medical errors.

One client from our Press Ganey Online Client Forum observed the following:

> Growing up with both a mother and father who were pharmacists running their own business, I learned that pharmacists can be an excellent source of information. Not a day went by that my parents didn't serve as a consultant to their customers. I think that a pharmacist might be more approachable to patients and they may give the perception that they have more time to discuss medication issues. Patients can be very overwhelmed at the number of medications they

---

[20] A. Calabrese, K. Cholka, S. Lenhard, B. McCarty, G. Zewe, D. Sunseri, M. Robers, and W. Kapoor, "Pharmacist Involvement in a Multidisciplinary Inpatient Medication Education Program," *American Journal of Health-System Pharmacy* 60 (2003): 1012-18.

[21] See *http://www.uky.edu/Pharmacy/news/Clinical Pharmacists.html* (Accessed November 1, 2006) and *http://www.mco-inc.com/collab0300.pdf* (Accessed November 1, 2006).

are on when leaving the hospital and a pharmacist can offer help about the best time to take medication, a good way to stay organized on the medication schedule, and of course, explain side effects.

☑ **More and more, hospitals are involving their pharmacists in quality improvement initiatives. Pharmacists can bring a lot to the table.**

Case Managers Ensure Medications Communication

Some facilities make medication review a part of their case managers' duties. For example, efforts at Claxton-Hepburn Medical Center (CHMC) in Ogdensburg, NY, to improve patient satisfaction included making changes to processes. CHMC identified a need to improve discharge planning from the question regarding help arranging home care services. In the past, case managers had focused their attention only on patients who met criteria for home care services. Based on patient feedback, CMHC expanded assistance in planning for discharge to all patients. Each patient receives a letter of introduction and visit from a case manager. A list of questions encourages patients and family to discuss concerns such as living environment, transportation, nutrition, prescriptions and payment for services.

☑ **Case managers also play an important role in making certain patients receive and understand the information they need.**

Give Patients their Medical Records

One Press Ganey hospital gives patients a copy of their bedside medication administration record. According to their nursing staff, patients feel more involved in their care. They saw the effectiveness of ongoing medication teaching improve while the time that it took to review instructions at discharge was shortened. They also implemented a standard to have physicians talk to patients about their medications—even if the physicians believe it to be redundant. After implementation, they found that the additional review helped. Finally, all of this improved discharge medication reconciliation.

☑ **Patients want to know what they're taking and what it can do to them. Sharing and reviewing the same information that you're working from is a great place to start.**

Include the Patient in Medication Decision-Making

Patients themselves have a key role to play in ensuring the safety of medical care. Improving communication with patients, listening to their concerns, and facilitating active partnerships should be central to any patient safety strategy.[22] In modern medicine, medications can be as big a part of the course of treatment as any other physical surgery or procedure. We would never order a patient to undergo a surgery without their consent. Likewise, we should be just as diligent with explaining medications, their side effects, and offering patients a choice of medications (or no medicine) to achieve their desired health outcomes.

What patients want to know is really not all that complex. Still, sometimes patients need help formulating the right questions to ask. Many patients will remain silent out of deference to the physician (e.g., the sentiment that the physician should know what to ask and it's not our place to question them). Others will be overcome with anxiety since they lack experience. To help patients overcome these obstacles, many leading hospitals are now implementing ASK ME3™.

Developed by the Partnership for Clear Health Communication®, ASK ME3 provides an explicit, easy-to-use method for overcoming health literacy problems. Three questions that *all* patients should ask their doctor, nurse, or pharmacist:

(1) What is my main problem?
(2) What do I need to do?
(3) Why is it important for me to do this?

Hospitals encourage patients to do this by including brochures, posters, and handouts in patients' literature as well as integrating the practice into standard communication for providers. Materials and information are available from the website: *www.askme3.org*

☑ **Give patients the tools, education, and courage to be full partners in their health care. Three questions, that providers will want to cover anyways, can't be asking too much.**

---

[22] Vincent CA, Coulter A. Patient safety: what about the patient? *Qual Saf Health Care* 2002;11:76-80.

Checklist: Medication Communication

The following is a checklist of proven tactics to improve communication regarding medications. For more details on any item, refer to the previous stories.

- Educate patients early and often. Get to elective surgery patients prior to admission with information and tools to assist in a clear dialogue on medications.
- Involve pharmacists heavily. Begin with a one unit pilot or simply high-risk patients.
- Explicitly add this to case managers' inventory for discharge planning.
- Give patients their medication records and review the medications list.
- Include patients in medication decision-making. Explore patients' goals for treatment and give options to meet their needs.
- Integrate communication tools into daily practice, such as ASK ME3.
- Include the HCAHPS questions in your nurses', nurse managers', and/or leaders' daily rounds. There is no reason why staff can't double-check with questions such as "I want to make sure that you've been given all the information you need. Have we told you about the medication your taking and any possible side effects?"

Chapter 8.

Global Ratings

How They're Measured

The "Global Ratings" are covered in two HCAHPS survey questions:

☑ Using any number from 0 to 10, where 0 is the worst hospital possible and 10 is the best hospital possible, what number would you use to rate this hospital's performance during your stay?

☑ Would you recommend this hospital to your friends and family?

For the first question, patients rate the hospital on a scale of 0 to 10. For the second question, patients use a four-point scale: Definitely No, Probably No, Probably Yes, and Definitely Yes.

The global rating of hospital care (0-10) will likely be the publicly reported measure that garners the most attention because it tends to be the easiest to understand.

The global rating of recommending the hospital to friends and family is the measure most predictive of patient loyalty, for example, positive or negative word-of-mouth and return-to-provider behaviors.

The Patient's Perspective

These two global ratings ask patients to step back and consider everything that happened during their hospital stay. Literally, anything can factor into these patient ratings. Possible influencers include the following: meals, family and visitor care, patient safety, emotional and spiritual care, admissions process, tests, therapies, insurance and payment handling, or other administrative procedures. Often, one memorable experience—negative or positive—will be the "moment of truth" that swings their vote into the highest or lowest possible rating. Global perspectives may have as much to do with the organization's culture as with the aggregation of every individual care episode.

Our Stories

Involve All Departments
By Kendra Ciszczon, Staff Consultant

I always suggest to clients when forming improvement committees, to try to include people from their billing, pharmacy, and security departments, as well as some of their auxiliary areas. I think this helps in two ways: First, it involves some of those departments that say they don't need to worry about the patient satisfaction scores (they typically argue that because their areas are not represented on the tool, they don't affect the results). They begin to see how they affect the organization as a whole and, in turn, patient satisfaction. Second, sometimes when we include only the people who work in the areas being focused on by the survey, we put up blinders to some "golden nuggets." We tend to say, "That is not possible because of this, this, or that." Or even argue, "We have tried that before and it didn't work . . ." People from other areas of the organization can sometimes bring in great ideas that would not have even been mentioned by the people who work in the actual area being rated.

> ☑ **Involve people and departments that you normally wouldn't consider in service or clinical quality issues. Their outside perspective may be exactly what's needed to shake things up.**

Family Needs: Chaplain Care
By Beth Heck, Regional Service Manager

I recently was on an extended visit to a large teaching facility. Each day I would wait in the lobby for my contact to come to take me to the conference room. On my first day there, I noticed a family of five sitting in the lobby. A woman was reading a magazine and four children were busy playing with toys. As I looked closer, I noticed they had a cooler and sleeping bags with them, but at the time I did not give this much thought. The next day I returned and the family was still sitting in the same area with all of their belongings. By the third day, I decided it was time to question what was happening. My contact explained that the father of the family was critically ill in the Intensive Care Unit (ICU) and the family lived more than an hour away. Instead of trying to visit him when possible, they had moved into the lobby of the hospital. The mother stayed in the ICU as long as possible and the woman in the lobby was the children's grandmother. My contact explained to me that everyone knew who the family was, that this was not allowed, and that they had gone through the process of having security trying to remove them every evening to no avail, which usually ended in an argument.

Later that day the chaplain of the facility was in a training session. When discussing the importance of patient's emotional needs, I brought up the story of the family in the lobby. After the session, the chaplain approached me and asked me to tell him more of the story I was discussing about the family. This was the first he had heard of this and asked me to take him and show him the family. When we entered the lobby, the chaplain went right to the grandmother and asked her to explain her situation. She told him that her son-in-law would most likely not live through the week, they wanted to make sure the children would be able to be with him as often as possible before he passed, and they had very little money to drive back and forth or try to stay in a hotel. Immediately after hearing this story, the chaplain excused himself and left.

The next day when I returned the family was gone. My first reaction was that security won the battle that evening and the family left. As I was leaving the hospital at the end of my visit, I saw the chaplain again. I asked about the family and then heard the rest of the story. When he excused himself, he called a local hotel and booked a room for the family to be billed to the facility. He then went to talk to the mother who was with the dying father to explain where the family would be staying and then drove everyone to the hotel himself. He went on to tell me that, to him, this was one small thing he could do for this suffering family, but that it meant everything to this family. He was not sure why no staff had approached him about this situation. They all know Chaplain Services had money budgeted for these situations, and he was concerned about other patients or families that may have had similar experiences. His parting comments to me were about what is truly important in life. The staff members were more concerned about the lobby looking disorderly with the family "living" there rather than the concern for each of the family members who were losing a loved one.

☑ **The difference between being patient-centered and facility-centered becomes clear when patient needs and facility needs come into conflict.**

Visitors and Family

Hospital regulations require a wheelchair for patients being discharged. While working as a student nurse, I found one elderly gentleman—already dressed and sitting on the bed with a suitcase at his feet—who insisted he didn't need my help to leave the hospital. After a chat about rules being rules, he reluctantly let me wheel him to the elevator. On the way down, I asked him if his wife was meeting him. "I don't know," he said. "She's still upstairs in the bathroom changing out of her hospital gown."

> ☑ **Although rules are in place for good reason, and should be adhered to, there are times that you should obtain more details about a given situation to appropriately proceed.**

Treating Emotional and Spiritual Needs

To improve patients' emotional and spiritual experience, Ephrata Community Hospital began incorporating complementary therapies into care and treatment modalities. The Mind Body Spirit Committee of the Complementary/Alternative Medicine Program decided a CD-based guided imagery program for use at each patient's bedside would be the most acceptable in the relatively conservative northern part of Lancaster County. The CDs combined guided imagery, soothing instrumental music, comforting voices, and environmental sounds to encourage patients to relax and ease emotional, mental, and physical distress. Two years later, a 5-CD Tranquilities Hospital Series and a CD player are at each bedside and are being utilized in many other departments.

Program Development

The program is designed to address the common experiences of hospital patients, such as worry, fear, pain, sleeplessness, and need for healing. In addition, the CDs respect the diversity of patient perspectives.

Training

Nursing units, respiratory, cardiology, housekeeping, surgery, emergency, social service, and other staff members were trained by the Chaplain on guided imagery and the benefits to patients. The staff was also given the opportunity to experience guided imagery.

Implementation

With hospital finances limited, the Chaplain, in cooperation with the Development Office, approached several area businesses for contributions to fund the program.

Success Stories

The hospital staff has witnessed many positive outcomes when using the CDs. The technique relaxes patients coming in for surgery, lowers patient blood pressure, is effectively used with Alzheimer's patients, and is calming for the hospital staff.

The connection of the mind, body, and spirit is very important in the healing process. This approach has proven to be effective and appropriate at Ephrata. The anecdotal evidence from clients, and the positive environment that the program creates for staff, correlates with rising customer satisfaction.

Customer Satisfaction

After one full year of use, Press Ganey scores that measure whether emotional and spiritual needs are being met, have increased. Ephrata's score went from 82.8, the year prior to implementing the program, to a current score of 84.3.

> ☑ **When you treat patients' bodies and heal physical needs, you win their respect. When you heal their emotional and spiritual needs, you win their hearts.**

Memorable Meals
By Martin Wright, Solutions Consultant

Patients with special or restricted diets often present challenges to hospitals. For patients on a special or restricted diet, one facility decided that, along with discharge papers, they would include some helpful tips for special diets. With each meal that came, a recipe was included for a low salt meal or something that fit that person's diet. If, for example, the patient got chicken cordon blue, without salt (not sure how that would happen, but it's just an example), for their meal, the meal tray would include a tent card describing how the chef prepared that meal within the limits of the diet. This gives the patient a takeaway recipe when they are discharged so that they can follow the diet at home. Also, upon discharge, a full cookbook for the patient's diet is available, if they need one.

> ☑ **Take advantage of synergistic opportunities like this to simultaneously promote your hospital's brand and health living while meeting patient needs.**

Tell Us about Yourself
By Martin Wright, Solutions Consultant

I worked with a hospital, the University Medical Center (Tucson, AZ), that has implemented a short preference survey at admission. The patient comes into the medical center, goes through the typical registration and admission process, and then, at the end of the admission process, is asked four questions similar to the following.

- One: What is your favorite restaurant?
- Two: What movie theater in town do you prefer?
- Three: What is your favorite food?
- Four: What is your favorite soda?

They then use the preferences of each admission in service recovery to create WOW opportunities.

> ☑ **Customizing service recovery to meet individual patients' unique needs and preferences takes service to the next level.**

Losing Wait
By Katie Drevs, System Consultant

Caritas Good Samaritan Medical Center (Brockton, MA) began tracking patient wait times in admitting. The average time was a discouraging 25 minutes. To improve wait times, the following changes were made:

- The information desk was modified to accommodate an admitting "greeter" who serves as the "air traffic controller" for arriving patients. This "controller" directs a patient to where they need to go quickly and efficiently.
- The department underwent a complete overhaul that included consolidating outpatient and inpatient admitting in one location.
- Extensive staff training included taking staff on tours to departments like radiology and surgery where the admitting team could meet and talk to their internal customers whose work schedules are greatly affected by the registration process.
- The department adopted a standard uniform for better identification. This allowed patients to quickly identify hospital personnel who could help get them to where they needed to go.

As a result of these improvements, wait times were reduced from *25 minutes to 5 minutes.*

The Valley Hospital (Ridgewood, NJ) completed a study in which they measured wait times. They determined that the average time patients spent waiting to be transported to an available bed was unacceptably long, with an average wait of 90 minutes. They found out that the transport staff were transporting a lot more than patients, which increased the turnaround time. After prioritizing the patient need, and developing a system of communication with bed control, wait times were reduced. They measure their progress by using a report card system with information posted weekly.

You may want to consider this best practice used in the family sitting area. To keep family members updated, every 30 minutes, have a nurse liaison go to the surgical suite, talk to the staff, and update the family. Valley Hospital is able to direct the family to the appropriate room because they have centralized scheduling and everything is coordinated in one place.

☑ **No one likes to wait. If you can, streamline processes to reduce wait times. If you can't reduce wait times, reduce the *perception* and *experience* of wait times by making it more comfortable and predictable.**

An Infant's Prints
By Kelly Wright, Staff Consultant

Having a baby is an exciting and memorable time for families. It's one time when a hospital stay isn't an inconvenience for the patient. After the mother delivers her baby (or babies), present her with a gift of her baby's prints. Create a plaque or shadowbox with the baby's footprint and handprint. This is a great keepsake for the family to take home with them and hang in the nursery.

☑ **Having a baby is one hospital visit people actually want. Make it memorable. Give them a keepsake of their magical experience.**

Got Insurance?
By Julie Piatkowski, Knowledge Assistant

When I was a young mother-to-be, I was extremely excited about the delivery of my first child. I did everything to prepare for the birth of my child: pre-registered for my hospital stay, participated in Lamaze classes, and toured the hospital delivery room and Neonatal Intensive Care Unit, so that the surrounding area would be familiar to me when I delivered my child. Once the big day arrived and I was in labor, I checked in at the front desk of the emergency room. I waited just a few minutes for a nurse to take me up to the Obstetrics Unit to get ready to deliver my first child. I was then taken into the delivery room to labor. The nursing staff hooked me up to the fetal monitors and an IV. As my labor progressed, the nurses would come in regularly to check on me and would periodically ask whether I had any questions. I never really had any until about seven hours into my labor when one nurse in particular came in to check on how far my labor had progressed and to inform me on how much longer it might be until I had a baby. I had a moment of shock as I realized that there may be a problem regarding the length of time I was in labor versus the total amount of time that the insurance company would allow me to stay and would pay for. I asked her, "How long can I stay in the hospital, since I have been here for abut 7 hours already. Will I have to leave in 17 hours?" The nurse looked at me funny and replied, "The only way you will leave the hospital in 24 hours is if you don't have insurance. DO you have insurance? You know, for being so young?" To this, I replied, "Of course! I pre-registered all of my information including insurance information and you should have it on file." I then proceeded to give her the name of my insurance. To my surprise, the nurse quickly took the fetal monitor off me, disconnected my IV, and told me I would have to wait to continue my labor while she checked to make sure I had insurance. Like anyone can wait during delivery. I was so mad that when the doctor came in I let her know what the nurse had done and said. I was again hooked up to the monitor, a new IV was connected, and I did not see that nurse again for the remainder of my delivery. I ended up having a beautiful baby boy. The delivery went well (considering) and everyone was healthy and happy.

> ☑ **Do not let your predispositions to culture, age, income level, religion, education level, and so on determine the quality of care given to a patient. These details, such as one's ability to pay, are secondary to obtaining the care they need to be happy and healthy.**

Just Ask Them!
By Beth Heck, Regional Service Manager

The easiest way to determine patient expectations from their stay in the hospital is to ask them. When a patient is admitted and moved to their room, one of the most important things is to walk through the information packet with the patient and any family members present. After showing them the information packet, ask two simple questions:

- What are you expecting from your stay with us?
- What is the most important thing you would like us to know?

I have heard many different answers to these questions ranging from "I expect to be able to walk again" from a man who was having a leg amputation, to "I do not want to be in any pain" from a woman having open-heart surgery. One woman's priority as relayed to us, was her desire to ensure that her husband had hot meals while she was away in the hospital.

Add these items to the whiteboards in the patient's room. This will allow every staff member to have up-front information on the patient's expectations. It is everyone's duty to help fulfill these expectations.

> ☑ **It is easy to get information on patient expectations.**

The Importance of First Impressions
By Beth Heck, Regional Service Manager

We all know that first impressions mean everything. Naples Community Hospital (NCH) in Naples, Florida, knows how to make a positive first impression. Last year, a colleague and I were visiting NCH for a few days of on-site education sessions for staff. When we arrived at the hospital, we walked to the front door. We saw a distinguished-looking gentleman standing outside the front door helping a woman into her car. Watching him, our first impression was that this was the CEO of the facility helping a patient. As we walked up, he stopped us and welcomed us to the hospital; he asked our names and how he could help us. At this point, we were still under the impression this was the CEO of NCH. He walked us inside and directed us to "his stand" and this is when we began to second-guess our first impressions. He called our contact and asked them to meet us in the lobby.

While we waited, we talked a little bit with the gentleman. He told us his name was Peter and that he was a volunteer at the hospital. He works as the greeter and information helper every day. When we explained to him that we were with Press Ganey, he showed us the survey that was showcased by the door and told us that he talks with every patient about the survey before they leave. As we waited, patients were coming and going. As people walked in the door, he would stop them, welcome them, and ask how he could help. When a patient would leave, he would ask them how their stay was, if there was anything that could have been done better for them, and if he could help them in any way before they left. He then asked them to fill out the survey when they received it because of its importance to the future development of NCH.

Each day at the facility, Peter would greet us with a smile, ask how our night was, and see whether there was anything he could do for us that day. Every night, Peter walked us out and asked if anything could have been done better. We watched him as he directed patients and visitors, helped people with any questions they had, called a cab for a person who needed a ride, and held a women's hand as she waited for her family to come.

Peter treated every person who entered NCH as a guest in his home. Walking in the door at NCH with Peter present made you feel like the most important person in the hospital. Peter's presence gives patients and visitors the impression that NCH cares about them. To this day, my colleague and I both talk about "Peter the Greeter" everywhere we go.

☑ **You can never take back a first impression. Patients and visitors will carry these impressions with them throughout their stay. It is hard to make up for a bad first impression, so you should start off with a bang.**

Sharing Data throughout the Organization
By Laura Lindberg, MS, CPHQ, Knowledge Manager

Sharing information in a large organization is a complex process and requires careful planning and assessment of the organization. Press Ganey has created its eCompass tool to allow multiple users access to data as quickly as the data become available. This allows clients to have the most up-to-date information from their patients.

The purpose of communicating is a continuum starting with sharing information and ending with shaping behavior. According to a *Health Management* article, (Fraser S. Spreading good practice; how to prepare the ground, *Health Management*, June 2000.) the more you desire to change behavior, the more personal the communication will be. Because most patient satisfaction data users are attempting to improve their scores, knowing the information is often not enough. At a presentation at the 2004 client conference, Sister Nika Lee illustrated *Info*EDGE®, which allows clients to drill down data and gain a deeper understanding of their patients' needs.[23] Paper reports do not allow for this type of data manipulation. If only a few people have access to the information, special reports and further analysis of the data can get caught in the bottleneck.

Although the initial training sessions for eCompass may be time-consuming, it gives ownership of the data to those responsible for patient satisfaction improvement and empowers them to find answers to their questions. The success of this effort depends partially on how well the organization adopts new technologies and the emphasis placed on patient satisfaction efforts.

Adding online users is only successful if they are properly trained and have the time to work with the data. It can be an excellent tool to engage more staff, but discontinuing paper reports may send the message that the data are no longer important. Planning a careful transition strategy and assessing the culture of the organization must be completed before any change in practice.

Press Ganey recommends allowing multiple users to the eCompass tool because it helps integrate the data and solutions information throughout the organization. Patient satisfaction is not just one person's responsibility but is everyone's. Yet allowing access to the tool will not lead to real change if it is not executed properly.

Another important benefit of allowing access to the data online is improving the timeliness to the data. Following are some client success stories that mention providing access to data on a monthly or even more frequent basis. Although

---

[23]   N. Lee, *eCompass: Taking Data to the Next Level*, Press Ganey Client Conference (2004). Available at *http://www.pressganey.com/products_services/readings_findings/ satmon/article.php?article_id=247* (Accessed November 1, 2006).

there are multiple methods of this distribution, providing eCompass to managers allows them to share data with their staff on a more frequent basis.

Allowing multiple users on eCompass has several benefits, such as the following:

- Enables more frequent access to current data
- Allows customized reports
- Offers the ability to further drill down data in areas of concern
- Empowers employees to find answers to their own questions
- Establishes proper ownership of patient satisfaction data

Yet any facility that wishes to have staff become more actively involved in analyzing their data must allocate the time, resources, and training for the employees to do so. An organizational assessment of its readiness to accept the responsibility, and thorough communication plans, are necessary to make a successful transition. When managers are committed to increasing the scores for patient satisfaction data—using the Press Ganey online analysis tool *Info*EDGE®—and make these expectations known to staff, the executive leadership's goals within the organization are reinforced.

☑ **Train managers and staff members who are leading the charge with patient satisfaction efforts on how to analyze the data using online reporting tools.**

The Importance of Buy-In from All Levels
By Amy Frederick, Lead Consultant

From my experience working with hospitals and conducting on-site visits, I am able to observe a lot about the hospital's culture just from walking up and down the halls. Our clients frequently ask for our advice to help create a patient-centered culture. There are many key drivers on the road to success when creating a patient-centered culture, but one of the most important steps is getting buy-in from all levels (e.g., CEOs, upper-level management, frontline staff, physicians, etc.). Many of our clients struggle with this, especially when they are trying to transition from a CEO that has been there for 30-some years to someone new, and everyone is used to doing things a certain way. People tend to be hesitant to make changes and it takes time for this change to happen. For progress to be made, there needs to be champions to take on the transition plan.

A few months ago, I visited a hospital to educate the staff, managers, and others on their survey results, which they were seeing for the first time. This was also the first time that this hospital had ever surveyed their patients, so the results were a bit shocking to see exactly what the patient's perspective was. They also soon realized that the patient's expectations weren't the same as 30 years ago. What was so effective about this visit was the turnout of the staff at every level. They had recently gotten a new CEO who had previously worked with Press Ganey at other hospitals, so he was familiar with patient satisfaction and the surveying of patients. The CEO went on to explain why everyone needs to be on board with this, and how it affects everyone working at the facility, even if they don't have direct contact with the patients. There were more than 100 attendees that all heard the same clear message from the CEO. He was taking the first step to creating a patient-centered culture, educating the staff on the importance of patient satisfaction. Of course, this will be a work in progress for them, but they have just received their second report and responses increased in almost every category. I have been working closely with the primary contact to determine a path for their success. Their goal is to have every service achieve a high percentile rank and be the best of the best.

☑ **Don't overlook the importance of buy-in for the staff to believe in a patient-centered culture.**

Everything Speaks
By Heather Frederick, System Consultant

I visited a facility a few months ago with a colleague to conduct patient satisfaction user education training for their managers. We had just finished our last session before lunch and decided to walk around the facility to find a place to eat. We figured the cafeteria would be busy and loud and we just wanted a place to sit quietly and collect our thoughts before our afternoon training sessions began. We ended up choosing a fast-food restaurant that was located inside the hospital. We proceeded to order and then sat down at a nearby table to wait for our number to be called to collect our food. I was disappointed in the interactions that I observed between the restaurant staff and their customers. They were rude and the service was extremely slow. A couple of customers even walked out grumbling about the poor the service and said they wanted nothing to do with eating there.

Later, I learned that the restaurant staff were not employed by the hospital, as the hospital has a contract with this particular restaurant. As a visitor, I associated the bad service I observed with the facility I was in and would still think so today if I was not told otherwise. I would be willing to bet that other visitors, patients, and family members do the same thing, because most likely they are not aware of the same knowledge I had. An experience like this could sway their scores negatively on survey questions about friendliness, timeliness, accommodations for family/friends, overall hospital experience, and whether they would recommend the facility or not. Everything speaks to the quality of your facility!

> ☑ **An experience (even a trivial one) that a patient, family member, or visitor may experience in your facility speaks to the quality of the facility. It may make the difference in how your facility is viewed. Nothing is too small to overlook.**

Employee Motivation and Education
By Beth Heck, Regional Service Manager

Many clients have asked me how to motivate their employees when it comes to patient satisfaction. When asked what they currently do, many told me they show the staff two things: (1) the current mean survey score and (2) the negative comments they received. My next question is always whether they know what a mean score really means and why they shared only the negative comments.

There are two obstacles to overcome in motivating your staff: (1) educating them on what the data really mean and (2) letting them know that not all patients that return surveys are unhappy. Make sure they are aware of every question on the survey. This is an open-book test, and staff need to know what questions patients are being asked. Teach all staff a basic understanding of the data being reported. Teach staff how the scale on the survey is translated to a 100-point scale, what a mean score is, how it is calculated, and how it relates to a percentile rank. Ensuring that all staff have this basic information will make them more accepting of the data.

Everyone has heard from their staff members that only unhappy patients return surveys. In visiting and speaking with many staff members, I have seen this trend. Many employees have said they are only told how bad their scores are and about negative comments from patients. There are ways to disprove this expectation. Show your staff the Top Box Analysis information. The Top Box shows all of the questions on the survey broken out by response frequency. This shows every "Very Poor to Very Good" that was answered for each question. The most important area to look at on this is the percentages of "Good" and "Very Good" responses. Every hospital, no matter where it is located, will see the majority of their patients score in these two categories. This means that the majority of patients are saying the hospital gave good care, and the patient was happy with their experience. The Top Box is not just about mean scores and percentile ranks, it also gives basic data about how patients rated each question, which can be powerful. Educating staff about these pages in the report will eliminate the theory that only the unhappy patients return surveys.

One of the simplest ways to motivate staff is to show them the positive comments that patients give on the survey. Focusing on negative comments will automatically give employees a negative attitude; no one wants to only hear about the bad things that may have happened. Sharing the positive comments will also provide learning opportunities for other staff members. Hearing what has been successful for others can be one of the best educational resources.

Lastly, it is important to reward and recognize staff. Celebrate even the smallest accomplishment. Positive reinforcement is an excellent motivational tool. Motivating staff can be a simple task; it only requires sharing the correct materials and educating them on those materials.

☑ **It is not difficult to move from a negative outlook of patient satisfaction to a positive one. People just need to be given the right information.**

Exceeding Expectations
By Renee Doren, MBA, System Consultant

Today, people can choose where they wish to receive their health care, just like people who travel choose their hotel stays. I travel to the Atlanta area quite a bit, but after one hotel experience, I will now only stay at the Holiday Inn Downtown location.

I checked into the hotel late in the evening, around 9:00 p.m. and the lobby was empty, except for the person who checked me in. She gave me my room key and told me if I was hungry, the restaurant would be open for about another hour. I went up to my room, put my luggage inside and went back downstairs to the restaurant for a quick bite to eat. I got back to my room at about 10:00 p.m. and noticed my message light was blinking. I retrieved the message, thinking it was just my husband checking to make sure I arrived safely.

To my surprise, however, it was the hotel's front desk person letting me know how long she would be on duty, asking me to call her if I needed a wake-up call, and letting me know that if there was anything I needed, because of my late arrival, I should call the front desk and she would take care of it. This exceeded my expectations and really made a difference in my hotel stay.

I tell this story to clients I visit on site as an example of service excellence. In health care, people can check patients into the ER, but if there is no follow-up or information provided, the patient and their family can feel like just another number. By doing something extra or above and beyond, your actions will stand out in their minds. Patients will then recommend you to others, return to your facility, and become part of your best marketing campaign.

☑ **Look to exceed customer expectations, no matter how small the gesture.**

Coffee Talk
By Tobeter Towne, Lead Consultant

I was in a small city in New Hampshire and I stopped at a McDonald's to get a cup of coffee. As I was standing in line, an elderly gentleman commented that I looked like a businesswoman. I replied that, yes, I was a consultant. He then asked what I consulted about. I told him that I visit hospitals and provide suggestions on what they need to do to increase patient satisfaction. He asked whether I was going to the hospital up the street. When I replied that I was, he said, "Good, because someone needs to straighten those people out."

☑ **You never know who in your community is talking about you and you never know what they are saying. Therefore, you need to make a positive impression on every patient, so that they speak well of you in the community.**

Secret Shopper
By Kelly Wright, Staff Consultant

When I was in high school, I worked at a retail store in our local mall. I was the typical teenage cashier, working a part-time job after school. Because the store wasn't seeing the sales that they had hoped for, they decided to install a "secret shopper" program. They hired someone to come in, shop around, try on clothes, and then make a purchase. This person would report back what they felt and saw as they went through this shopping experience. It really helped the store managers to see what they couldn't see when they weren't out on the floor. When the managers were around, the service from the employees was great, because they were always trying to impress management. But when managers weren't around, the service wasn't always the best. Having a secret shopper helped them to analyze where breakdowns were occurring and identify areas that were lacking in service. The employee whose number was on the sales receipt then would receive recognition for positive scores. These employees had a greater incentive to try harder for each and every customer that walked through the door.

The same idea can be applied to a health care setting. It could be something as small as calling the various departments or the information desk to monitor their phone etiquette. Are they friendly all the time, even at busy times? Do they give their name and location? Do they offer to help and project the feeling that they mean it? Volunteers in the organization, which wouldn't cost the facility any money, could do this. Or, a firm could be outsourced to go through a typical procedure. They could come in for tests, X-rays, and other procedures.

The "patient" could then monitor how friendly staff were, whether they treated them with respect, whether they informed them about their condition and treatment, and so on. This would allow management to really see how their staff were treating the patients and to pinpoint the areas in which they were lacking that service excellence. This process is especially helpful as facilities work on specific initiatives. They can track these initiatives and "check up" on them to see whether their new processes are working.

☑ **Management can't always be around for each patient, and they can't always be there to monitor how they are being treated. Have a secret shopper be the eyes for management from an outsider's point of view.**

Snack Time
By Kelly Wright, Staff Consultant

Patients may not always have the opportunity to eat at normal meal times. They may be admitted late at night or early in the morning, have tests scheduled during meal times, or just might not be hungry at the time that the meals are served. Have different "snack boxes" available for the patients in between meals. If they are hungry or unable to eat when their meal is served, they can grab smaller items to eat before their next meal.

☑ **Patients are not always able to eat when meals are normally scheduled, but this shouldn't prohibit them from eating when they are hungry. A backup plan is needed for these situations.**

Give Them What They Want
By Beth Heck, Regional Service Manager

Today, it seems that every hospital struggles with the issue of patients who are on special diets. Most patients, no matter their status, believe they are on a special diet because it is not the food they are used to eating at home. One of the hardest groups to please is the younger demographic group. When a person is used to fast food and restaurants, being given a meal they do not choose automatically causes dissatisfaction. To combat this issue, many hospitals have turned to menu-style meals. Patients are given menus daily with foods that fit within their diet requirements and a phone number to place an order. Many hospitals have started adding more options for patients (e.g., salads, sandwiches, and pizza) that are available daily.

Hospitals that have implemented this have seen increases in their satisfaction with meals. Throughout a stay, patients have little to say about what happens to them. A major impact of menu-style meals is that the patient is given a choice in something that is happening to them during their stay and giving them back some of the control they may feel they have lost.

> ☑ **Standards for amenities are rapidly changing in the healthcare industry. More and more, hospitals now provide room service-like meal service and private rooms. Some facilities may need to play catch-up to these trends.**

Special Diet Food Cards
By Kelly Wright, Staff Consultant

When my grandfather was in the hospital for his heart attack, he was placed on a low sodium diet. Trying to explain to my grandmother what she could and couldn't cook, what my grandpa could and couldn't eat, and what to look for on the labels became quite a task. To add to this task, my grandmother was expected to remember everything.

She needed a ready-made packet for patients and family to take home with them based on the specific diet of the patient. This would have given her something to consult when deciding on the next meal or what to buy at the grocery store. She really needed explicit instructions about what he could and couldn't have. She also needed a card, or something small, that she could have carried in her purse. When she went shopping for the food that he could eat, she then would have had the security of knowing exactly how to determine what to buy in the face of all of the food labels.

> ☑ **Have a food and nutrition explanation packet available for patients who are on a special diet to ensure that they understand and follow the instructions after they leave the hospital.**

It's about People, Not the Task
By Shelley Barger, Staff Consultant

One January, when I was still in management with Target®, the store was in post-Christmas mode and payroll was extremely tight commensurate with the soft sales and high refunds. We were getting ready for Valentines Day, and valentines needed to be merchandised on the checkout lanes. The best person for this job was Jennifer. She was terrific at whatever job she was given—cashier, service desk, cash office, or merchandising (all of it). She was fast, reliable, and accurate—a triple threat in retail.

I asked her to merchandise the checkout lanes with soft, red and pink, puffy hearts of all kinds. Jennifer completed the checkout lanes with the finesse and speed anyone would expect of her. She did a fabulous job.

Now, I knew that Jennifer's boyfriend and she were breaking up. It didn't occur to me, however, that being immersed in valentines might be a little difficult for her emotionally. My awareness of this fact was buried somewhere in the task at hand. She told me later that it had been hard for her to work on the valentines—that she was feeling sad and here I had thoughtlessly given her the job of merchandising the valentines.

What a gift she gave me to be more aware of people's feelings.

Jennifer now works in my hometown grocery store (merchandising, of course, health and beauty aids). I saw her just last night when my daughter and I picked up some groceries. Who would have thought that Jennifer would end up being so close to me?

> ☑ **Time for a conscience tune-up. Remember, people—not the tasks—are what it is all about.**

Reward and Recognition Ideas
By Renee Doren, MBA, System Consultant

What better way to foster staff or employee motivation than to provide them with rewards and recognition for providing exceptional customer service or for going above and beyond?

I have visited clients and have seen quite a few reward and recognition practices that you may want to adopt in your organization. These suggestions can be tweaked according to your organization's policies and procedures:

- One facility adopted a program in which employees can recognize other staff performing in a way that goes above and beyond normal day-to-day activities. The staff member who witnesses the event fills out a "nomination card" and sends it to that person's supervisor. Once the staff member receives six nominations, they are awarded with an hour off with pay. For every six nominations, the employee is entered into a drawing at the end of the year, for additional prizes (movie passes, gift cards to local restaurants, and so on).
- Whenever an employee's name is positively mentioned in the comment section of a patient satisfaction survey at another facility, the supervisor makes a copy of the comment and puts it on the bulletin board in the staff lounge. The comments are rotated on a regular basis, usually monthly. Posting positive comments reinforces expected behavior and promotes motivation in others.
- Another facility recognized that their staff worked hard, and that they rarely had time to eat or take a break. Overall, they had no time for themselves. So as a way to reward them for their hard work, each nursing

unit or work area was equipped with their version of a "first aid kit." The kits contain Advil®, Aleve®, sanitary napkins, Tylenol®, sticks of gum, candy bars, change for the pop/soda machine, packets of tissues, breakfast bars, vouchers for coffee/latte at the cafeteria, etc.

- On a quarterly basis, all staff who were positively recognized in survey comments receive a signed letter from the CEO thanking them for their actions. Also, they are invited to have lunch with the CEO and to offer any suggestions for improvement in their customer service excellence standards. This feedback from staff is valuable to any CEO or senior management team because the staff can see things they can't, and they see it on a daily basis.

☑ **Rewarding staff motivates them to perform the behavior over and over again, as well as motivates others. Recognizing staff lets them know they are appreciated and valued.**

Sweet Secrets to Service Success: Getting Creative with Educational Programs

What better way to communicate and reinforce service principles than with candy? The list below can help stimulate ideas for your service excellence program. You might distribute a candy bar with a short inspirational saying or thank you note as a simple means of rewarding and recognizing staff. Some managers will place candy in a communal dish with an appreciative "themed" thank you note. Still others will bring candy to a staff meeting and use its theme as a starting point for discussion. Following are some ways you can creatively use sweets:

100 Grand Bar® (Payday®)
Start conversations about how great service can benefit the bottom line and how it is related to our paychecks. It also can be used as a reminder that a kind word can make you feel like a million bucks.

Almond Joy® (Nutter Butter®)
Sometimes the best ideas are the "nuttiest ones." This candy can show people that we appreciate their "nutty" sense of humor.

Bit 'o Honey®
We don't have to like all of our patients or coworkers, but just try giving them a little bit of honey. As the saying goes, you catch more flies with honey.

Butterfingers®
Talk about how service is dependent on good handoffs between departments. How can you avoid "butterfingers"?

Carefree® Gum

What do patients want? They want a "carefree" stay. But, they also want a lot of care from us. Also, the gum may be carefree, but our work is serious as we touch scared and vulnerable people every day.

Charms Blow-Pops®/Lollipops

Charm, friendliness, and good attitude—these are the keys to providing great service. Patients want us to have charm and be filled with good stuff on the inside.

EXTRA® Gum

A reminder that **great** service comes from making a little bit of extra effort every day—particularly to be better than our competitors and on days that we just don't feel like it—because that's what clients deserve.

Good and Plenty®

What patients and families deserve to think about our staff: that we're good and there are plenty of us.

Hershey's Hugs® and Kisses®

Illustrate the point that we don't just want to be "cared for." We want to be "cared about."

Hot Tamales® (Red-Hot Dollars®)

Use in conjunction with "service recovery" discussions. Learn how to handle the folks who've become "red-hot," so they don't cost you unnecessary dollars.

Ice Breaker Gum®

Learn the importance of making new employees and patients feel welcome. Go out of your way to break the ice and welcome them.

Jolly Joes® (Jolly Ranchers®)

Remind everyone of how wonderful it is to have colleagues that remain upbeat, despite the stresses of the day. That's the type of caregiver that patients want.

Kudos® (Granola Bars)

Everyone needs to feel appreciated. Saying thank you goes a long way toward letting others know that they aren't taken for granted.

LifeSavers®

Make the point that we have important jobs. No matter what your individual position is, our work matters.

Mounds®

We sometimes have "mounds" of work to do. Recognize the extra effort that staff make to help each other out.

Nestle Crunch®

A reminder that providing good service is easy during a slow day, but it's much harder to concentrate on service and teamwork during "crunch" time.

Skor®

Discuss how to "skor" big with patients and families and remind staff that it is sometimes the little things that make a big difference.

Smarties®

Given for learning something new or mastering a new skill. Or distribute them to everyone because the whole group is already "smart." This is about adding to what you already know.

Snickers® (Chuckles®, Laffy Taffy®)

Although the work we do is serious, a little bit of humor (a snicker, chuckle, or laugh) goes a long way toward making our days easier.

Starburst®

This illustrates the kind of Wow! that patients want. What can we do to get great results?

SweetTarts®

The "SweetTart" theory is proof that you can be two things at once. We need to be good at the technical part of our jobs and the interpersonal side, too.

Symphony® Bars

Everyone in a symphony plays a different part, but it is everyone playing his or her best together that makes beautiful music. Also, musicians have to listen to a conductor to bring out the best. No instrument is more important than any other. What is "music to our ears" as employees, as patients, as managers, as colleagues?

Three Musketeers®

It's all for one and one for all. Teamwork is a key to service success.

Treasures®

This is how we need to treat our patients: to remember that they are treasures to their families. This can also be used to discuss why it is important to integrate new employees into the organization well—again, because they are such treasures.

Whoppers®

Use to celebrate a "Whopper of an Idea" or a "Whopper of an Effort."

☑ **Anyone can take a moment to thank a coworker for a job well done. These simply provide a fun vehicle for doing so.**

One Thing

For your facility, the HCAHPS survey may present a host of behavior and service changes. You may need to change the way you do things on dozens of different activities. Trying to change many things at once typically doesn't work.

Many successful Press Ganey clients focus on one issue, question, or behavior every quarter or month. By focusing on just one improvement activity, it enables greater insight. You'll be able to see the effects of that one change. You'll be able to observe the degree to which units and staff members actually adopt that one practice. Managers will be able to concentrate on changing whatever processes and systems need to be changed to enable adoption of that one practice. Staff will be able to focus their efforts on changing their one behavior in the appropriate situations instead of trying to think about doing a dozen new things.

For example, Thomas Hospital (Fairhope, AL) made a key part of their comprehensive improvement program the "Behavior of the Month" with videos and posters featuring the behavior. Hospital employees wrote scripts, acted in and directed videos that emphasized a particular customer service behavior. The Behavior of the Month posters, placed throughout the hospital, served as reminders.

☑ **Discover the power of focus. Concentrate all employees' improvement energies on one issue. Many hands make light work.**

Checklist: Global Perceptions

The big picture can be intimidating. We've culled it down to the following action list:

- Patient satisfaction depends on employee satisfaction. Employees will treat patients only as good as they're treated. Start by making certain you're taking care of your troops.

- One way to take care of each other is to reward and recognize your peers. Leaders and managers aren't the only people who can recognize good work. Often, a respected peer saying, "Good job" is more meaningful.
- Food is an undeniable necessity and an intimate part of our human experience. Although it may be lower priority than clinical excellence or positive human interactions, good meals can create positive emotions and a memorable experience. Consider the following:

    ☑ Investing in room service
    ☑ Tactics to address special diet issues
    ☑ Comfort foods on the unit for quick, easy access
    ☑ Partnering with local restaurants
    ☑ Encouraging healthy lifestyles through hospital-branded recipes

- Examine your communication practices. If no one knows your improvement priorities, no one can do anything about it. If know one knows what needs to change, nothing will happen. Change begins with awareness. Share information with abandon.

    ☑ Make this an agenda item for every staff meeting.
    ☑ Use every medium possible, including:

        - Bulletin boards
        - Intranet
        - Internet or hospital website
        - Employee open forums
        - Staff areas or break rooms
        - Newsletter
        - Press releases
        - Handouts
        - Staff meetings
        - Large plasma screens or computer screens
        - Custom printed items (e.g., banners)

    ☑ Give all managers access to eCompass
    ☑ Give all managers this book.
    ☑ Test awareness by asking random employees to identify your major patient satisfaction improvement priorities. If they don't know, it's not going change.

- Understand *your patients'* expectations and exceed them. *Your* patients mean not simply the population in your community, but every individual.

People are unique and you won't know how to wow them if you don't ask.

- Remember the emotional impact of hospitalization. Emotional and spiritual care matters to the long-term loyalty and feelings about your hospital.
- Get outside perspectives!

  - ☑ Involve new people from other departments.
  - ☑ Get a secret shopper to come in.
  - ☑ Ask friends or other non-hospital employees to walk through the facility and tell you what they see and hear.
  - ☑ Read and act upon the comments from your Press Ganey patient satisfaction surveys.
  - ☑ Get former patients to participate in focus groups.

- Get creative! Just because something is not in a book doesn't mean it's not a great idea. Just because someone else hasn't done it doesn't mean you can't do it. In fact, the best ideas are often the ones that no one has tried yet. If you're the first to do something—that's competitive advantage!

Chapter 9.

Conclusion

A call light goes off nearby. Respond. Get water. Give pain medication. Find the television remote. Got it. Move. Call them, get that, move this. Check, check, check. Done. Move on.

What if there was a call light for addressing our own needs for growth, learning, and personal development? What if a call light went off, we walked into a room and we had to do three things for self-improvement? When you think about it, that's exactly what a customer survey is all about. The results are the voices of other people identifying the areas in our work that could help us perform better.

HCAHPS and Press Ganey surveys offer an opportunity for reflection. Our world is so fast-paced and demanding that we rarely have the time to take a moment to think about what we've done. Survey results hold a mirror up to our organization, our team, and us individually as care providers. Without feedback, we never know about the effects our words and actions have on others. Press Ganey provides a structured feedback system designed to help you, your team, and your organization improve by providing a better understanding of the impact your care has on patients.

When we see the expectations inherent in those survey questions, we have a choice. We can dismiss the implicit expectations and refuse to change. Or, we can align ourselves with the needs of those we serve and reaffirm our dedication to continuously improving ourselves and our organization. Listening to others, empathizing, and changing ourselves to respond and better help others—this represents the best of humanity. When we shut down, refuse to listen, make excuses, and decide to do things the same way we've always done, we forego a valuable opportunity. Patients may lose the joy and comfort of an inspirational healing experience. Ultimately, we lose even more. We lose the opportunity to become something greater than ourselves. We lose the chance to be a beacon of hope to an ailing patient and family. We lose the joy of expressing complete compassion for fellow humans.

In our modern age, it's easy to become complacent. Often, we confuse comfort with happiness. Being average is easy and comfortable. Being truly great takes courage, hard work, and persistence. We may rationalize the easy route and tell ourselves we're content with the status quo, but secretly, unconsciously, our soul yearns for a challenge. Every year at Press Ganey's National Client Conference, we meet thousands of healthcare professionals from across the United States come to share and learn ways to improve health care. All who attend the conference truly want to improve, the people who overflow with joy are those who are either exceptionally high performers or striving hard to get there. The secret is they're not happy because they're performing well. Their happiness comes from the work itself, the *act* of consistently going above and beyond expectations. It's the journey, not the destination that makes all the difference.

High performance in serving patients isn't just for the patients. It's for our own good. It's for our own happiness. Our daily work can be a joyous, soulful expression of ourselves to living life to the fullest. What do patients love? Patients love being part of an experience where everyone involved finds themselves truly fulfilled.

So now, you've completed this book. You've absorbed the collective wisdom and experience of dozens of Press Ganey consultants and hundreds of Press Ganey's best clients. Now what?

The next step is your decision and the actions you take to follow-through on that decision. Will you answer the call light?

Appendix A

Hospital CAHPS®

> Please use black or blue ink to
> fill in the circle completely.
> Example: ●

YOUR CARE FROM NURSES

1. During this hospital stay, how often did nurses treat you with <u>courtesy and respect</u>?
   - ○ Never
   - ○ Sometimes
   - ○ Usually
   - ○ Always

2. During this hospital stay, how often did nurses <u>listen carefully to you</u>?
   - ○ Never
   - ○ Sometimes
   - ○ Usually
   - ○ Always

3. During this hospital stay, how often did nurses <u>explain things</u> in a way you could understand?
   - ○ Never
   - ○ Sometimes
   - ○ Usually
   - ○ Always

4. During this hospital stay, after you pressed the call button, how often did you get help as soon as you wanted it?
   - ○ Never
   - ○ Sometimes
   - ○ Usually
   - ○ Always
   - ○ I never pressed the call button

YOUR CARE FROM DOCTORS

5. During this hospital stay, how often did doctors treat you with <u>courtesy and respect</u>?
   - ○ Never
   - ○ Sometimes
   - ○ Usually
   - ○ Always

6. During this hospital stay, how often did doctors <u>listen carefully to you</u>?
   - ○ Never
   - ○ Sometimes
   - ○ Usually
   - ○ Always

7. During this hospital stay, how often did doctors <u>explain things</u> in a way you could understand?
   - ○ Never
   - ○ Sometimes
   - ○ Usually
   - ○ Always

THE HOSPITAL ENVIRONMENT

8. During this hospital stay, how often were your room and bathroom kept clean?
   - ○ Never
   - ○ Sometimes
   - ○ Usually
   - ○ Always

9. During this hospital stay, how often was the area around your room quiet at night?
   - ○ Never
   - ○ Sometimes
   - ○ Usually
   - ○ Always

YOUR EXPERIENCES IN THIS HOSPITAL

10. During this hospital stay, did you need help from nurses or other hospital staff in getting to the bathroom or in using a bedpan?
    - ○ Yes
    - ○ No   **If No, Go to Question 12**

11. How often did you get help in getting to the bathroom or in using a bedpan as soon as you wanted?
    - ○ Never
    - ○ Sometimes
    - ○ Usually
    - ○ Always

12. During this hospital stay, did you need medicine for pain?
    - ○ Yes
    - ○ No   **If No, Go to Question 15**

13. During this hospital stay, how often was your pain well controlled?
    - ○ Never
    - ○ Sometimes
    - ○ Usually
    - ○ Always

14. During this hospital stay, how often did the hospital staff do everything they could to help you with your pain?
    - ○ Never
    - ○ Sometimes
    - ○ Usually
    - ○ Always

127

15. During this hospital stay, were you given any medicine that you had not taken before?
○ Yes
○ No **If No, Go to Question 18**

16. Before giving you any new medicine, how often did hospital staff tell you what the medicine was for?
○ Never
○ Sometimes
○ Usually
○ Always

17. Before giving you any new medicine, how often did hospital staff describe possible side effects in a way you could understand?
○ Never
○ Sometimes
○ Usually
○ Always

WHEN YOU LEFT THE HOSPITAL

18. After you left the hospital, did you go directly to your own home, to someone else's home, or to another health facility?
○ Own home
○ Someone else's home
○ Another health facility **If Another, Go to Question 21**

19. During this hospital stay, did doctors, nurses or other hospital staff talk with you about whether you would have the help you needed when you left the hospital?
○ Yes
○ No

20. During this hospital stay, did you get information in writing about what symptoms or health problems to look out for after you left the hospital?
○ Yes
○ No

OVERALL RATING OF HOSPITAL

Please answer the following questions about your stay at the hospital named on the cover. Do not include any other hospital stay in your answers.

21. Using any number from 0 to 10, where 0 is the worst hospital possible and 10 is the best hospital possible, what number would you use to rate this hospital during your stay?

○ 0 Worst hospital possible
○ 1
○ 2
○ 3
○ 4
○ 5
○ 6
○ 7
○ 8
○ 9
○ 10 Best hospital possible

22. Would you recommend this hospital to your friends and family?
○ Definitely no
○ Probably no
○ Probably yes
○ Definitely yes

ABOUT YOU

There are only a few remaining items left.

23. In general, how would you rate your overall health?
○ Excellent
○ Very Good
○ Good
○ Fair
○ Poor

24. What is the highest grade or level of school that you have <u>completed</u>?
○ 8th grade or less
○ Some high school, but did not graduate
○ High school graduate or GED
○ Some college or 2-year degree
○ 4-year college graduate
○ More than 4-year college degree

25. Are you of Spanish, Hispanic or Latino origin or descent?
○ No, not Spanish/Hispanic/Latino
○ Yes, Puerto Rican
○ Yes, Mexican, Mexican American, Chicano
○ Yes, Cuban
○ Yes, other Spanish/Hispanic/Latino

26. What is your race? Please choose one or more.
○ White
○ Black or African American
○ Asian
○ Native Hawaiian or other Pacific Islander
○ American Indian or Alaska Native

27. What language do you <u>mainly</u> speak at home?
○ English
○ Spanish
○ Some other language (please print):

_____

THANK YOU
Please return the completed survey in the postage-paid envelope.